THE GRAMMAR
OF MATHEMATICS

THE GRAMMAR OF MATHEMATICS

LINCOLN K. DURST
Claremont Men's College

ADDISON-WESLEY PUBLISHING COMPANY

Reading, Massachusetts · Menlo Park, California · London · Don Mills, Ontario

This book is in the
ADDISON-WESLEY SERIES IN INTRODUCTORY MATHEMATICS

Consulting Editors: Gail S. Young and Richard S. Pieters

PREFACE

This book was written for an elementary course, whose only prerequisites are a sound knowledge of high school mathematics, a critical attitude, and a willingness to think about things. The subject matter is the language of mathematics, mathematical abstraction, and proof.

As teachers know, and students will admit, too many people have more trouble with mathematics than anybody deserves. Some of the trouble apparently stems from the fact that mathematicians seem to have their own language and their own way of looking at things. Certainly nobody can deny the existence of a problem of communication. This book is predicated on the idea that a discussion of language can help to give some appreciation of mathematics.

A classic example is the definition of limit, which often comes as quite a jolt to calculus students. Here is a sentence like none the student was ever asked to parse in any class in grammar; he is told, however, that he should understand it and is expected to show that he does, often by being asked to produce on quizzes some proofs in which it is used. It is no secret, among those who read such quizzes, that this procedure is not a roaring success.

No less a mathematician than John von Neumann is supposed to have said that we never really understand things, we just get used to them. But some things must be easier to get used to than others. Consider limits again: f has limit l at a is defined by a "six-dimensional" condition. Three of the six variables (ϵ, δ, x) are quantified and three (f, l, a) are not; what is worse, the "open sentence" involved contains an implication. The fact that inequalities and absolute values also appear is probably the least of the difficulties, in view of the formidable logical structure of the sentence. Some progress is being made. Absolute values and inequalities are now getting more emphasis in the schools, and some programs even talk about open sentences. But more remains to be done in the way of getting this indigestible mass divided into chunks the patient can swallow. Here we try to do just that. No one who has ever asked his students to "negate" the condition that f have limit l at a is likely to doubt that the difficulty is very largely linguistic.

We examine the language of mathematics and, because we treat the subject from a mathematical point of view, we are able to use it as an example of mathematics itself. With this example before us, we can draw some conclusions about the abstract nature of mathematics: conclusions one can draw only by examining some abstract system.

Many students encounter a major discontinuity in their work when they get to the point at which they are expected to construct mathematical proofs in algebra and analysis courses. Some have suggested that the jump might be less abrupt if this problem were tackled seriously in high school algebra courses. Others would postpone the question to upper-division courses in the college curriculum. One suggestion that has been made is to offer a "transition" course designed to bridge the gap. This book was written to provide just such a bridge: it was developed in connection with a number of courses over a period of several years. Preliminary versions have been used with honors classes of high school students, with college freshmen, and with in-service secondary school teachers.

We apply our study of grammar to the analysis of proofs which, for many students, are among the greatest of mysteries. Our contention is that proofs are proofs because of their grammatical structure. This idea is not at all new: it has been around for as long as people have discussed logic. Frequently in elementary courses earnest, sometimes vigorous, efforts are made to "make mathematics meaningful." Such efforts are, of course, important for they can be very illuminating; but perhaps, like many things, it is possible to carry them too far. Considerations of "meaning" help to explain what a given theorem is all about, how it can be used, and, hence, why anybody should consider it interesting enough to want to try to prove it. But it may be conceivable that too much emphasis on meaning actually constitutes an obstacle to learning what makes proofs what they are.

We say that some string of statements constitutes a proof simply because of the way the "sentence structure" of each statement is related to that of the other statements in the string. Proofs, then, are formal things: they depend directly on the structure of statements, and thus only indirectly on their meaning. *What* one may choose to discuss is more or less irrelevant—what is important is *how* he states his case. This thesis is one of the main themes of the book: indeed, it summarizes what logic has to say about deductive argument and proof. But, precisely because we are interested in using it to analyze proofs, we must treat logic as we would treat any other branch of applied mathematics: with a good deal of attention given to how logic itself is to be interpreted.

This is not the first book to analyze proofs and it is certain not to be the last. We offer what amounts to just one rule of "inference," rather than a vast arsenal of rules. Readers interested in more formal treatments of the subject can go on to read some of the standard logic texts: with an idea of what logicians try to accomplish, they may better appreciate some of the details of more technical presentations.

This book owes much to many people. My own logic teachers were E. T. Bell and Hans Reichenbach. Many colleagues at Rice University did much to stimulate and encourage my efforts, among them Arlen Brown, Gerald MacLane, Alan Robinson, Arthur Ullman, and Trenton Wann. Jack Conner, Robert Dilworth, and John Kenelly read early versions of the manuscript and have made some valuable suggestions. To all these men I owe great debts of gratitude: debts I may have managed to repay by producing a book which might just contain nothing that any of them would be willing to claim as his own.

I am indebted to Rice University not only for giving me the opportunity to experiment with this material but also for granting me a leave of absence to work on the manuscript. I am also indebted to Claremont Men's College and to the California Institute of Technology, where much of the writing was done. My greatest obligation, however, is to my wife for all she has been willing to tolerate, from start to finish.

Claremont, California   Lincoln K. Durst
March 1969

CONTENTS

INTRODUCTION

Our subject is grammar. We are interested in the language of mathematics and especially in the structure of the kinds of statements occurring in mathematics. However, nearly everything we shall find to say about the language of mathematics is relevant to the language of any other domain of thought. Thus what we undertake here might be described more broadly as a study of careful and precise communication.

Our approach is quite different from that of traditional grammar. Therefore we indicate here, in broad outline, how we attack the problem.

We begin, not by breaking statements down to examine their internal parts, but rather with a study of how given statements may be combined with one another to form new and more complicated statements. This is the subject matter of Chapter 1. This part of logic has been aptly described as the "molecular theory" of statements. In Chapter 2 we lay the foundation for our study, in Chapter 3, of the internal structure of "atomic" statements. In Chapter 4 we apply our results to some topics in mathematics.

We begin with an analysis that is blatantly oversimplified: in Chapter 1 we classify statements in only two categories (True, False) and deliberately ignore all the more subtle considerations which we might expect to be relevant to an adequate analysis of language. We must therefore anticipate that what we can say in the context of this oversimplification cannot be all of what we would like to say about language, nor can it be all that we ought to say. And if some of the things that we do say in Chapter 1 seem peculiar, one should not be too surprised: one must expect peculiarities, even absurdities, in any inadequate analysis.

Inadequate as it may be for analyzing language, the "algebra" we develop in Chapter 1 will prove to be extremely important for our work in Chapter 2 and for our more refined analysis of language in Chapter 3. How this works out will appear as we proceed, and provides an excellent illustration of the remarkable power of mathematical abstraction.

CHAPTER ONE

ALGEBRA OF STATEMENTS

In this chapter we make frequent use of the words *statement, true,* and *false,* although we never define these terms. Since this procedure may strike some readers as bizarre, we begin by examining it.

In the first place, no definition is worth giving unless the term being defined is explained using only terms which are in some sense simpler. In the second place, one can never define every term relevant to any subject of discourse without encountering one of two difficulties: Either a chain of definitions is circular (so that, for example, *A* is defined in terms of *B*, *B* in terms of *C*, *C* in terms of *D*, etc., *Y* in terms of *Z*, and *Z* in terms of *A*), or it never ends. Neither of these alternatives is tolerable. The first brings one back to where he started, not really any better informed than when he began; and the second requires more activity than any human can survive.

The escape from this dilemma is to call a halt to definitions at some "appropriate" place in the process, leaving some terms "undefined." As an example, consider elementary plane geometry. The various geometrical figures, triangles, rectangles, circles, etc., are all defined in terms of points and lines. The words *point* and *line*, however, are not defined. In lieu of definitions for *point* and *line*, one begins with a list of "axioms" or "postulates" telling all one is supposed to know about how these terms are to be used.

Although we leave the terms *statement, true,* and *false* undefined, we require that their use be governed by the following pair of rules or "laws":

1. *Law of the Excluded Middle (tertium non datur):*
   Each statement is either true or false.

2. *Law of Contradiction:*
   No statement is both true and false.

Statements in English are ordinarily expressed in declarative sentences. Just what a declarative sentence may be and which declarative sentences qualify as statements seem to be matters of opinion, taste, and controversy. Thus, even if two people should agree that

Virtue is green or it is triangular.

is a declarative sentence they may disagree on whether it is a statement (i.e., either true or false, but not both) and why. And even if they agree that it is a statement, they may disagree on whether it is true or whether it is false. Another example, equally controversial, is

Caesar is a prime number.

The following example is much less controversial since many people seem to agree that it meets our pair of requirements:

A Democratic administration is better for the country than a Republican administration.

Everyone who votes in a national election expresses his belief that both requirements are met. The results of such elections show, however, that there can be wide disagreement on whether or not a statement is true, even when there is wide agreement that it is indeed a statement in our sense.

Pronouns often play a role similar to that of "variables" or "unknowns" in algebra. Thus the sentence

He is an honorable man.

can be either true or false, depending on the man under discussion; just as

$$x^2 - 3x + 2 = 0$$

is true if x denotes either 1 or 2 but is false for every other "value" of x. Sentences like these, which are "sometimes" true and "sometimes" false, are not examples of statements because they fail to meet our criteria: we demand of a statement that it be either definitely true or definitely false, but not both—not sometimes one, sometimes the other. One can, of course, convert such sentences into statements by specifying x, or by saying who "he" is:

Brutus is an honorable man,

$$0^2 - 3 \cdot 0 + 2 = 0, \quad 1^2 - 3 \cdot 1 + 2 = 0, \quad \text{etc.}$$

Not all sentences containing pronouns fail to be statements. Thus

If someone has a million dollars, he is rich.

For any real number x, either x > 0 or x ≤ 0.

The use of pronouns and unknowns is part of the study of the "internal structure" of statements. These matters are discussed in some detail in Chapter 3.

Even though we concentrate on statements, we seldom worry about whether individual "simple" statements are true. In mathematics we are often concerned with combinations of statements, or relations between statements, such as assertions of the form *if a, then b,* where *a* and *b* are statements themselves. Whether or not either of *a* and *b* is true is often irrelevant, the real question being whether *b* follows from *a.* The following statement is an excellent example:

> *If there are more people in the world with hair on their head than there are hairs on any one person's head, then there are two people in the world with the same number of hairs on their heads.*

This statement illustrates a fact of great importance; but its validity has nothing to do either with the number of people in the world, or with how many hairs there may be on anybody's head. Suppose we imagine all people who are not bald arranged in queues according to the number of hairs on their heads: one queue for those with just one hair, another for those with just two, etc., and finally a queue for the person(s) with the hairiest head(s) in the world. The statement above asserts that some queue contains more than one person if the number of people in the queues exceeds the number of queues.

1. COMPOUND STATEMENTS

In this section we discuss several ways one may form "compound" statements by modifying or combining given statements, we introduce letters to represent statements, and we lay the groundwork for an "algebra" of statements.

The first operation we consider is called *negation.* The negation of

Twice 2 is 4

is

Twice 2 is not 4,

and the negation of

9 is a prime

is

9 is not a prime.

Any statement in English may be negated by prefixing the phrase

It is not the case that.

The result, however, is often rather cumbrous. Usually it is an easy matter to insert *not* in an appropriate place. Thus in the examples just given we put *not* after the verb *is*. There are examples which are more complicated: the negation of

Each even number greater than 2 is the sum of two primes

cannot be obtained by putting *not* after *is*, unless *each* is changed to *some* or to *at least one*. (Examples like the last one are discussed in Chapter 3.)

If a is a statement, we shall write $\sim a$ for the negation of a. The following table,

a	$\sim a$
T	F
F	T

depicts the relation between the "truth values" of a and $\sim a$: $\sim a$ is false if a is true, and $\sim a$ is true if a is false.

We next consider the connectives *and* and *or*.

The *conjunction* of two English statements may be obtained by running them together with *and* between them. Thus

Roses are red and violets are blue.

If a and b are statements, we write $a \wedge b$ for their conjunction. Table 1.1 exhibits the dependence of the truth values of $a \wedge b$ on those of a and b:

TABLE 1.1

a	b	$a \wedge b$
T	T	T
T	F	F
F	T	F
F	F	F

Thus $a \wedge b$ is true when both of a, b are true; it is false when at least one of a, b is false. The conjunction $a \wedge b$ is often rendered in English using the connective *but* rather than *and* between the components a, b. Thus, according to Ogden Nash,

Candy
Is dandy
But liquor
Is quicker.

When we turn to *or* the problem is more complicated than with *not* and *and*. *Or* is used in two different ways in English and it is important that

TABLE 1.2		
Inclusive *or*		
a	b	$a \vee b$
T	T	T
T	F	T
F	T	T
F	F	F

TABLE 1.3		
Exclusive *or*		
a	b	$a \veebar b$
T	T	F
T	F	T
F	T	T
F	F	F

we distinguish between them.   One use is called "inclusive," the other "exclusive."   (In Latin, separate words are used: *vel* for inclusive *or*, *aut* for exclusive *or*.)   Tables 1.2 and 1.3 exhibit the difference.   Note that $a \vee b$ is true when at least one of a, b is true, and false only when both of a, b are false.   On the other hand, $a \veebar b$ is true when exactly one of a, b is true and false when a and b have the same truth value (either both T, or both F).   The tables indicate that $a \vee b$ is true whenever $a \veebar b$ is true, so $a \vee b$ may be taken as an understatement for $a \veebar b$.

If he wishes to do so, a writer of English can make his intention explicit by putting *a or b, or both* in the inclusive case, and *a or b, but not both* in the exclusive case.   He may also put just *a or b* and leave the distinction for the reader to try to make.   For example

An elevator can go up or down.

An escalator can go up or down.

Readers know (from experience) that an elevator does both.   Some escalators do too, but many do not.   Such a distinction if made by the reader is based on something not actually in the sentence: the reader's knowledge perhaps, and sometimes the context in which the sentence appears.   Consider

Don Juan's soul can go up, or it can go down.

In the context of the cosmography of *Paradise Lost* the *or* is exclusive; in that of *Man and Superman*, inclusive.   Unless the distinction is actually made by the writer within the sentence itself, the reader always has the right to interpret *or* in the inclusive sense.   If anything outside the sentence yields the distinction, it will do so in any case.   These observations apply to mathematics as well as to literature and conversation: if a writer does not add *but not both*, perhaps he is willing to let his reader decide what he should mean, but maybe he doesn't care.   In the second paragraph of page 1, we find the sentence

Either a chain of definitions is circular, or it never ends.

TABLE 1.4

a	b	c	$a \vee b$	$(a \vee b) \vee c$
T	T	T	T	T
T	T	F	T	T
T	F	T	T	T
T	F	F	T	T
F	T	T	T	T
F	T	F	T	T
F	F	T	F	T
F	F	F	F	F

TABLE 1.5

a	b	c	$a \underline{\vee} b$	$(a \underline{\vee} b) \underline{\vee} c$
T	T	T	F	T
T	T	F	F	F
T	F	T	T	F
T	F	F	T	T
F	T	T	T	F
F	T	F	T	T
F	F	T	F	T
F	F	F	F	F

Whether or not a circular chain ends is irrelevant, at least for the argument in the second paragraph of page 1. Consider, however, the two laws quoted in the fourth paragraph of page 1. Together they assert that the alternatives are exclusive, even if we take the *or* in the first one to be inclusive. A more interesting question is this: how should we interpret the three instances of *or* in the examples mentioned in the first sentence of this paragraph:

a or b, or both,

a or b, but not both.

Inclusive or exclusive? (Cf. Exercise 4, below.)

When the number of alternatives is more than two, the exclusive *or* is not as exclusive as some might guess. Consider *a or b, or c.* If *or* here is inclusive, we write $(a \vee b) \vee c$; if it is exclusive, $(a \underline{\vee} b) \underline{\vee} c$. We may construct tables (Tables 1.4 and 1.5) for these combinations in two steps, using Tables 1.2 and 1.3. Observe that $(a \vee b) \vee c$ is true if at least one of a, b, c is true, and false only if all three are false. But $(a \underline{\vee} b) \underline{\vee} c$ is true if exactly one of a, b, c is true, or if all three are true; and false otherwise. For a list of any number ($n \geq 2$) of alternatives,

$$a_1 \text{ or } a_2, \text{ or } a_3, \ldots, \text{ or } a_n,$$

the results are these:

Inclusive case:

> T if at least one of $a_1, a_2, \ldots, a_n$ is T,
> F otherwise.

Exclusive case:

> T if an odd number of $a_1, a_2, \ldots, a_n$ is T,
> F otherwise.

Thus the exclusive *or* can be used to assert that precisely one of a number of statements is true only when the number is two.

The so-called *trichotomy* property of inequalities (cf. Section 2, Chapter 4) involves three exclusive alternatives: of the three, any one may hold, but no more than one may hold. In order to state this property, one has to say this in so many words. Because such examples are rare in mathematics, there is really no need to treat them on any but an individual basis.

For these reasons *or* is nearly always used in mathematics in the inclusive sense. We shall call $a \vee b$ the *disjunction* of a and b. When we have occasion to mention it, we shall call $a \veebar b$ the *exclusive disjunction* of a and b.

EXERCISES

1. Construct truth tables for each of the following compounds:
    (a) $a \wedge (\sim b)$
    (b) $[a \vee (\sim b)] \wedge [(\sim a) \vee b]$
    (c) $[a \wedge (\sim b)] \vee [(\sim a) \wedge b]$
    (d) $(\sim a) \vee b$.

2. Construct tables for each of the following pairs of compounds and verify that for each pair the resulting columns are identical:
    (a) $a \wedge b$, $\sim[(\sim a) \vee (\sim b)]$
    (b) $\sim(a \wedge b)$, $(\sim a) \vee (\sim b)$
    (c) $a \vee b$, $a \vee ((\sim a) \wedge b)$
    (d) $a \vee (a \wedge b)$, $a \wedge (a \vee b)$.

3. Same as 2. (Truth tables with eight rows are required here because there are three component statements in each of the compounds.)
    (a) $a \wedge (b \vee c)$, $(a \wedge b) \vee (a \wedge c)$
    (b) $a \wedge (b \veebar c)$, $(a \wedge b) \veebar (a \wedge c)$
    (c) $[(a \wedge b) \vee (a \wedge c)] \vee (b \wedge c)$, $[(a \vee b) \wedge (a \vee c)] \wedge (b \vee c)$

4. Construct tables for

$$(a \vee b) \vee (a \wedge b), \quad (a \veebar b) \veebar (a \wedge b),$$
$$(a \vee b) \wedge [\sim(a \wedge b)], \quad (a \veebar b) \wedge [\sim(a \wedge b)],$$

and compare them with those for $a \vee b$, $a \veebar b$.

5. By assigning letters ($a, b, c, \ldots$) to their components, give symbolic versions of each of the following compound "statements":

(a) God said Let there be light: and there was light.
(b) The bells they do ring, and the birds they do sing.
(c) Love mourned long, and sorrowed after hope.
(d) His horse is slain, and all on foot he fights.
(e) Rescue, fair lord, or else the day is lost!
(f) Either be patient, and entreat me fair,
Or with the clamorous report of war
Thus will I drown your exclamations.

6. Many compound statements, not actually containing the words *and, or* may be considered as disguised conjunctions or disjunctions. For example, *No tickee, no washee* has the sense of $a \vee (\sim b)$, where a: *tickee*, b: *washee. Either you have a ticket, or you get no wash.* (Here it is clear that *or* must be inclusive, since the customer has to pay for his laundry as well as produce the ticket before he can get it.) Express each of the following sentences as a conjunction or a disjunction:

(a) Waste not, want not.
(b) History is neither dull nor easy.
(c) Private property [shall not] be taken for public use, without just compensation.
(d) You must study Plato in order to understand Aristotle.
(e) Ne'er throughout the year to church thou go'st,
Except it be to pray against thy foes.
(f) The prisoner will escape unless the cell is locked.
(g) The prisoner will not escape unless the cell is unlocked.

2. LOGICAL EQUIVALENCE

Negation, conjunction, and the disjunctions are related to statements in much the same way that arithmetical operations (addition, multiplication, etc.) are related to numbers. Just as the sum and product of two numbers are again numbers, the conjunction and disjunction of two statements are again statements. Our objects in this section are to examine this analogy and to exploit it.

Elementary algebra is intimately related to arithmetic. We examine briefly the connection between them, in order to emphasize their similarities and differences. Arithmetic deals with numbers and involves the manipulation of "numerals" representing them. There is considerable emphasis on "computation rules": methods for performing additions, multiplications, long divisions, etc. Algebra, on the other hand, involves the manipulation of "free symbols" (a, b, x, y, etc.) which are intended to represent numbers. Any given numeral is the name of a very definite number which is unequivocally identified by that numeral. An algebraic symbol may also be interpreted as representing some specific number, *but it need not be.* The point is that the symbolic manipulations of algebra have a validity independent of what particular numbers the symbols involved may stand for. For example, the correctness of the algebraic assertion

$$(x + y - z)^2 = (x + y)^2 - z(2x + 2y - z)$$

is entirely independent of what numbers the free symbols x, y, and z may be considered as representing. The connection between arithmetic and algebra is this: If each free symbol in an algebraic assertion be replaced by any numeral whatever, the result is a statement of arithmetic. For example, put 2, 3, 4 for x, y, z, respectively, above:

$$(2 + 3 - 4)^2 = (2 + 3)^2 - 4(2 \cdot 2 + 2 \cdot 3 - 4),$$

or more compactly, $1^2 = 5^2 - 4 \cdot 6$.

This way of using free symbols is characteristic of algebra, it represents the basic difference between algebra and arithmetic, and it is what makes algebra so much more powerful and economical than arithmetic. A single formula or theorem of algebra encompasses an infinity of arithmetical statements—all that may be obtained from it by substituting numerals for the symbols.

TABLE 1.6

p	q	$\sim p$	$p \wedge q$	$p \vee q$
T	T	F	T	T
T	F	F	F	T
F	T	T	F	T
F	F	T	F	F

In the last section we examined ways to alter or combine statements to form "compound" statements. If we liken those "operations" to arithmetical operations, our program in this section amounts to constructing the corresponding algebraic theory. By analogy with elementary algebra, we shall think of our "symbols" p, q, r, $\ldots$, not as representing specific individual statements as a, b, c, etc., did in the previous section, but as *free*, or *arbitrary*, statement symbols. We consider such a symbol capable of being replaced by any expression representing any specific statement. We define $\sim p$, $p \wedge q$, $p \vee q$ by means of Table 1.6. These tables express the truth value of the compound statement resulting from each of these expressions in terms of the truth values of statements used to replace the symbols.

We shall refer to any finite expression which can be constructed from free statement symbols, using these operations, as a *statement form*:

(1) Each free symbol is a statement form

(2) If A and B are statement forms, so are

$$\sim (A), \qquad (A) \wedge (B), \qquad (A) \vee (B).$$

Every form has associated with it a truth table column, each of whose entries is T or F. Such a column may be written with 2^n entries, where n is any integer not less than the number of symbols appearing in the form; the entries may be computed in step-by-step fashion using Table 1.6.

One of the necessities in any algebraic system is some kind of "equality" relation. We have seen (Exercise 2, Section 1) that $a \wedge b$ and $\sim[(\sim a) \vee (\sim b)]$ have identical truth table columns. With this example, and others like it, as guides, we introduce the notion of *logical equivalence* of forms, denote it by $\equiv$, and write

$$p \wedge q \equiv \sim[(\sim p) \vee (\sim q)].$$

Two forms are logically equivalent if they obtain the same truth value for all possible substitutions for their symbols. In the example under consideration there are just two symbols (p, q) and hence there are four types of substitutions with different combinations of truth values. Each of these types is represented by one row of a truth table. Thus p and q may both be replaced by true statements (T T), by a true statement and a false statement, respectively (T F), a false statement and a true statement, respectively (F T), or both by false statements (F F).

For combinations, such as $p \vee (q \wedge r)$, with three symbols there are eight types of substitutions, represented in the following list:

$$
\begin{array}{ccc}
\text{T T T} & \quad & \text{F T T} \\
\text{T T F} & \quad & \text{F T F} \\
\text{T F T} & \quad & \text{F F T} \\
\text{T F F} & \quad & \text{F F F}
\end{array}
$$

With each additional symbol, the number of types is doubled; thus there are 2^n types for n symbols.

Having the relation of logical equivalence we may raise a number of questions suggested by elementary algebra. In the algebra of numbers the operations of addition and multiplication are both commutative and associative,

$$x + y = y + x, \qquad\qquad xy = yx,$$
$$x + (y + z) = (x + y) + z, \qquad x(yz) = (xy)z;$$

and there is a distributive law,

$$x(y + z) = xy + xz.$$

It turns out that, in the algebra of statements, conjunction and disjunction are both commutative and associative:

$$p \wedge q \equiv q \wedge p, \qquad\qquad p \vee q \equiv q \vee p,$$
$$p \wedge (q \wedge r) \equiv (p \wedge q) \wedge r, \qquad p \vee (q \vee r) \equiv (p \vee q) \vee r.$$

TABLE 1.7

p	q	r	$p \wedge q$	$q \wedge r$	$(p \wedge q) \wedge r$	$p \wedge (q \wedge r)$
T	T	T	T	T	T	T
T	T	F	T	F	F	F
T	F	T	F	F	F	F
T	F	F	F	F	F	F
F	T	T	F	T	F	F
F	T	F	F	F	F	F
F	F	T	F	F	F	F
F	F	F	F	F	F	F

These equivalences may all be established by recourse to truth tables. All of them should seem quite reasonable on the basis of their linguistic interpretations. Although such interpretations can be reassuring, it is—after all— only the truth tables which we may take for authority: The operations were all defined by means of such tables, as was the notion of logical equivalence. Interpretation in logic has the same status as in geometry. In geometry once a theorem has been proved it may be interpreted as saying something about figures, although such interpretations are not permitted in the proof itself (they are described disparagingly as "arguing from the figure").

As an example of a proof using truth tables we exhibit Table 1.7 for the associative law for conjunction. Since the last two columns are identical, we assert

$$(p \wedge q) \wedge r \equiv p \wedge (q \wedge r).$$

We leave the other associative law and the commutative laws as exercises and turn instead to other laws. Just as one does in elementary algebra, we take the associative laws as license to omit parentheses and write simply $p \wedge q \wedge r$, and $p \vee q \vee r$. According to the associative laws it does not matter where parentheses are inserted: the results are equivalent.

In the algebra of statements both of the following *distributive* laws hold:

$$p \wedge (q \vee r) \equiv (p \wedge q) \vee (p \wedge r),$$
$$p \vee (q \wedge r) \equiv (p \vee q) \wedge (p \vee r).$$

Two very important laws of the algebra of statements are

$$\sim(p \vee q) \equiv (\sim p) \wedge (\sim q),$$
$$\sim(p \wedge q) \equiv (\sim p) \vee (\sim q);$$

they are called *De Morgan's laws*. Another fundamental law is the *law of involution*

$$\sim(\sim p) \equiv p,$$

often called the principle of "double negation."

There are a number of other basic laws which require a pair of special terms. The truth table column for the form $p \vee (\sim p)$ contains T's only, and that for $p \wedge (\sim p)$ contains F's only. Such forms are called, respectively, *tautologies* and *contradictions*. All tautologies are equivalent (they have the same column in their table) and all contradictions are equivalent (for the same reason). Because they are quite important it is convenient to have special symbols to represent a tautology and a contradiction. We shall use I and O, respectively. Thus I represents a truth table column having only T's, and O represents a column having only F's. We then have the four *identity* laws

$$p \wedge I \equiv p, \qquad p \vee O \equiv p,$$
$$p \wedge O \equiv O, \qquad p \vee I \equiv I;$$

and the four *complement* laws

$$\sim O \equiv I, \qquad\qquad \sim I \equiv O,$$
$$p \wedge (\sim p) \equiv O, \qquad p \vee (\sim p) \equiv I.$$

Observe that the third and fourth complement laws are symbolic versions of the law of contradiction and of the *tertium non datur*, respectively.

With two more laws we shall have completed our basic list. These two are called the *idempotent laws*:

$$p \wedge p \equiv p, \qquad p \vee p \equiv p.$$

It is worth noting and emphasizing that by shifting our attention from statements to forms, we are making an abstraction that is no trivial matter. As we indicated at the beginning of this section this abstraction is quite analogous to the step from elementary arithmetic to algebra. We no longer concentrate on individual conjunctions such as *Roses are red and violets are blue*, but on the statement form $p \wedge q$ which we allow to have no meaning beyond that granted by its truth table. For purposes of interpretation, we think of the form $p \wedge q$ as embodying everything that all conjunctions have in common and nothing more. Similar remarks apply, of course, to disjunctions, negations, and each of the other compound statement forms we have considered up to this point or will meet in later sections.

Abstraction is a kind of simplification: we lump together a number of things having something in common and ignore any distinguishing features they may possess. Such abstraction is worthwhile if it enables one to organize knowledge in an efficient and useful way. The advantages of elementary algebra are well known; it will be our task to show that the algebra of statements enjoys similar virtues.

The value of an abstract study must be reckoned by balancing whatever advantages it may have against the obvious fact that it is quite incapable of resolving any of the distinctions which were ignored so that it could be created. Our algebra of statements is based on a "truth functional" definition of statement connectives: we refer only to the "truth" or "falsity" of statements and their compounds. We deliberately ignore every other attribute a statement may possess, excepting only that we feel entitled to insist that a statement be unequivocal. The price we pay for generality may seem high— we have yet to see that it is not exorbitant.

The fundamental requirement of unrestricted substitution for our symbols can lead to combinations which seem strange. Thus from $p \wedge q$ we may obtain the following instances

> *Snow is black and sugar is sweet.*
>
> *Plato was Athenian, but Aristotle was wise.*
>
> *Squares are rectangles, and virtue always triumphs.*

Rhetorical etiquette may discourage such combinations on the grounds that the components are ill-matched or fail to be "parallel," but that cannot be taken as an indictment against our requirement of unrestrained substitution. It is the purpose of our algebra of statements to supply a fund of equivalences. He who would specialize them in outlandish ways must assume the responsibility for such quaint results as he may obtain.

The only method mentioned up to this point for establishing equivalences in the algebra of statements requires truth table verification. We are now in a position to announce some good news! Once we have established the so-called "basic" laws mentioned above, we need never bother with truth tables again. All the other laws of the algebra of statements can be derived from them by "algebraic manipulation." Such techniques are discussed in Section 4.

We collect our basic laws in a single list for easy reference:

BASIC LAWS OF THE ALGEBRA OF STATEMENTS

Identity: $\quad p \wedge I \equiv p, \qquad\qquad p \vee O \equiv p$

$\qquad\qquad\qquad p \wedge O \equiv O, \qquad\qquad p \vee I \equiv I$

Idempotence: $\quad p \wedge p \equiv p, \qquad\qquad p \vee p \equiv p$

Involution: $\qquad\qquad \sim(\sim p) \equiv p$

Complement: $\qquad \sim O \equiv I, \qquad\qquad\qquad \sim I \equiv O$

$\qquad\qquad\quad p \wedge (\sim p) \equiv O, \qquad p \vee (\sim p) \equiv I$

Commutative: $\quad p \wedge q \equiv q \wedge p, \qquad p \vee q \equiv q \vee p$

Associative: $\quad p \wedge (q \wedge r) \equiv (p \wedge q) \wedge r,$

$\qquad\qquad\quad p \vee (q \vee r) \equiv (p \vee q) \vee r$

Distributive: $\quad p \wedge (q \vee r) \equiv (p \wedge q) \vee (p \wedge r),$

$\qquad\qquad\quad p \vee (q \wedge r) \equiv (p \vee q) \wedge (p \vee r)$

De Morgan: $\qquad \sim(p \wedge q) \equiv (\sim p) \vee (\sim q),$

$\qquad\qquad\quad \sim(p \vee q) \equiv (\sim p) \wedge (\sim q)$

EXERCISES

Use truth tables:

1. Prove the commutative laws for conjunction and disjunction.
2. Prove the associative law for disjunction.
3. Prove both of the distributive laws involving $\wedge$, $\vee$.
4. Prove De Morgan's laws.
5. Prove that exclusive disjunction ($\underline{\vee}$) is commutative and associative.
6. Exercise 3 of Section 1 shows that conjunction "distributes" over exclusive disjunction:

$$p \wedge (q \underline{\vee} r) \equiv (p \wedge q) \underline{\vee} (p \wedge r).$$

Determine whether or not exclusive disjunction distributes over conjunction, over disjunction.

3. IMPLICATION

We have mentioned only the connectives *and*, *or*, and *not*. A reasonable question at this point might be: What others deserve consideration? Since we are confined at present solely to a consideration of truth values, we are able to answer the question without much difficulty. Each form we have studied is determined by a distribution of T's and F's in a column of a truth table. If we consider all the possibilities arising from a pair of symbols, we find there are only 16 of them (Table 1.8).

TABLE 1.8

p q	1	2	3	4	5	6	7	8	9	10	11	12	13	14	15	16
T T	T	T	T	T	T	T	T	T	F	F	F	F	F	F	F	F
T F	T	T	T	T	F	F	F	F	F	T	T	T	T	F	F	F	F
F T	T	T	F	F	T	T	F	F	T	T	F	F	T	T	F	F
F F	T	F	T	F	T	F	T	F	T	F	T	F	T	F	T	F

From our previous work the following columns are easily identified:

2: $p \vee q$	8: $p \wedge q$	10: $p \underline{\vee} q$
4: p	6: q	1: I
15: $\sim(p \vee q)$	9: $\sim(p \wedge q)$	7: $\sim(p \underline{\vee} q)$
13: $\sim p$	11: $\sim q$	16: O

Thus only four remain to be considered (3, 5, 12, 14) and, of these, two are the negations of the other two. It will suffice, then, to examine, say, only 3 and 5. If we write (tentatively) $p * q$ for 5, then 3 is simply $q * p$. Hence the whole question will be settled once we have disposed of 5. It is an easy matter to verify that column 5 represents the form $(\sim p) \vee q$ (Table 1.9).

TABLE 1.9

p	q	$\sim p$	$(\sim p) \vee q$
T	T	F	T
T	F	F	F
F	T	T	T
F	F	T	T

The combination $(\sim a) \vee b$ is of special interest. Observe that whenever both (i) a is true and (ii) $(\sim a) \vee b$ is true, then b must also be true. This suggests that $(\sim a) \vee b$ may bear some relation to the verbal expression *if a, then b* commonly used to indicate that statement b is a "consequence" of statement a.

Let us turn the question around: let us suppose that *if p, then q* is a compound statement form which can be represented by a column of T's and F's, and determine what that column must be. Two very modest requirements are enough to tell us all the entries:

(1) *if p, then q* is not a tautology,

(2) *if p $\wedge$ q, then p* is a tautology.

Our first requirement assures us that at least one entry in the column for *if p, then q* is F: it rules out only the possibility that every statement is a "consequence" of every other statement. Our second requirement is also quite tame: any statement *is* a "consequence" of its conjunction with any statement. Thus "given" both a and b, a "follows," no matter what statements a and b are. The second requirement determines Table 1.10, from which we see that *if p, then q* has three T's in its column, corresponding to the three combinations TT, FT, FF for p, q. The other entry, corresponding to TF, must be the F that we need. Thus we have determined all the entries. We adopt the notation $p \Rightarrow q$ for *if p, then q* and summarize this discussion in a truth table (Table 1.11). The expression $p \Rightarrow q$ is often read *p implies q*.

TABLE 1.10		
$p \wedge q$	p	*if p $\wedge$ q, then p*
T	T	T
F	T	T
F	F	T
F	F	T

TABLE 1.11		
p	q	$p \Rightarrow q$
T	T	T
T	F	F
F	T	T
F	F	T

For this reason, the compound form $p \Rightarrow q$ will be called an *implication*; p will be called its *hypothesis* and q its *conclusion*. Other common English renditions of $p \Rightarrow q$ are *q if p* and *p only if q*.

Because $p \Rightarrow q$ has been defined to be $(\sim p) \vee q$, the expression $a \Rightarrow b$ stands for the compound statement *not a, or b, or both*. Some examples of statements having the form $a \Rightarrow b$ are

> *If algebra is easy, trigonometry is dull.*
> *If all triangles are equilateral, then all triangles are isosceles.*
> *If* $1 = 2$, *then* $3 = 3$.

Whether the first is true is a matter of opinion: it amounts to

> *Algebra is not easy, or trigonometry is dull.*

The others are clearly true (their hypotheses are false):

> *Some triangles are not equilateral, or all are isosceles.*
> *Either* $1 \neq 2$ *or* $3 = 3$.

It must be observed immediately that only a few mathematical theorems actually have the form $a \Rightarrow b$, where a and b are *statements*. The "hypothesis" and "conclusion" of a theorem are very often linked by means of pronouns; for example,

> *If two triangles have corresponding angles congruent, then they are similar triangles.*
> *If* $x > 0$, *then* $x^2 > 0$.

Because of the pronouns linking them, the hypothesis and the conclusion cannot stand alone as statements. (This question properly belongs in Chapter 3, where it is discussed in some detail.)

We may not conclude, however, that the compound statement $a \Rightarrow b$ is never really used. It is, in fact, used quite often—and in precisely the sense we have given it. Consider the example from the introductory section of this chapter:

> *If there are more people in the world with hair on their head than there are hairs on any one person's head, then there are two people in the world with the same number of hairs on their heads.*

Here a and b are indeed statements; the compound statement merely asserts that at least one of the following alternatives holds: $\sim a$, or b.

> *If the incumbent is reelected, I'll eat my hat*

is another example of an implication between statements—which, indeed, is intended to be interpreted as an emphatic way of affirming the speaker's belief that the incumbent will not be reelected. Parents' admonitions to youngsters are a rich source of similar examples:

If you soil your dress, I won't give you any ice cream with supper.

If you don't stop sticking needles in your little sister, I'll send you to your room.

More examples can be found in Shakespeare's *Henry IV*: implication between statements is one of Sir John Falstaff's favorite forms of expression. Such implications are also popular with soothsayers, which may or may not have much to do with the fact that many are notorious for being thought cryptic. Thus

> *Macbeth shall never vanquished be until*
> *Great Birnam Wood to high Dunsinane Hill*
> *Shall come against him.*

This is certainly an "implication," though not phrased with the rather prosaic wording so popular among mathematicians.

In Section 6, we begin our discussion of "inference": the theory of drawing "conclusions" from "assumptions," or "premises." We shall find that the process of inference is based on what we call "tautological implications": tautologies of the form $A \Rightarrow B$, where A and B are statement forms. Some of the simpler examples of such tautologies are

$$p \Rightarrow p,$$
$$(p \wedge q) \Rightarrow p,$$
$$p \Rightarrow (p \vee q).$$

If the expression $A \Rightarrow B$ is a tautology, it is impossible to assign T, F to the symbols appearing in it in such a way that the conclusion is false when the hypothesis is true (cf. Table 1.11, the truth table for $\Rightarrow$). Thus, in tautological implications, we begin to find some of the "coherence" between hypothesis and conclusion often associated with conversational usage of the word *implies*. Much stronger forms of such coherence between hypothesis and conclusion will appear in Chapter 3, where we analyze the "internal" structure of statements.

The form $q \Rightarrow p$ is called the *converse* of $p \Rightarrow q$. Observe that these forms are *not* equivalent. (That is, implication is not commutative.) The form $(\sim q) \Rightarrow (\sim p)$ is called the *contrapositive* of $p \Rightarrow q$. These two *are* equivalent (cf. Exercise 2, below) and the fact that they are is the basis for one version of the method of proof "by contradiction."

The conjunction of $p \Rightarrow q$ and its converse $q \Rightarrow p$ is abbreviated $p \Leftrightarrow q$.

Definition $p \Leftrightarrow q = (p \Rightarrow q) \wedge (q \Rightarrow p).$

The double arrow $\Leftrightarrow$ is customarily read *if and only if*. It is easy to verify that $p \Leftrightarrow q$ has T's in the first and fourth rows of its truth table and F's in the second and third. Thus

$$p \Leftrightarrow q \equiv \sim(p \veebar q), \quad \text{or} \quad p \veebar q \equiv \sim(p \Leftrightarrow q).$$

For this reason, we may dispense with $\veebar$ entirely.

There is an important connection between equivalence ($\equiv$) and "two-way" implication ($\Leftrightarrow$) which we shall find useful in many problems. Suppose, indeed, that A and B are equivalent statement forms: $A \equiv B$. Then the compound form $A \Leftrightarrow B$ is a tautology. Conversely, if $A \Leftrightarrow B$ is a tautology, then A and B are equivalent. For if $A \equiv B$, any replacement of the symbols in A, B yields statements A_0, B_0 with the same truth value (TT or FF). Thus $A_0 \Rightarrow B_0$ and $B_0 \Rightarrow A_0$ are both true, and so is their conjunction: that is, $A \Leftrightarrow B$ is a tautology, since any replacement for its symbols yields a true statement. Conversely, if $A \Leftrightarrow B$ is a tautology, any replacement of its symbols yields a pair A_0, B_0 of compound statements with the same truth value: $A \equiv B$.

Thus we can write a good many tautologies without further ado: put a double arrow between the two sides of any equivalence. For example,

$$p \wedge q \Leftrightarrow q \wedge p,$$
$$\sim(p \wedge q) \Leftrightarrow (\sim p) \vee (\sim q),$$

etc. We also get tautologies if we use a "one-way" arrow instead. We shall have more to say about this idea—in later sections we shall have occasion to exploit it frequently.

Sooner or later in every discussion of logic something is done to curb the proliferation of parentheses. Nearly every writer has his own set of rules and there is little uniformity among them: readers consulting more than one source must take care to check the conventions of notation in each.

We have already observed that associative laws justify the omission of the parentheses in expressions like

$$\{[p \vee (q \vee r)] \vee (p \vee q)\} \vee (p \vee r).$$

We may avoid the use of other parentheses by special conventions. Examples familiar in elementary algebra are the conventions

$$ab + c \quad \text{represents} \quad (ab) + c, \quad \text{not} \quad a(b + c),$$
$$-a + b \quad \text{represents} \quad (-a) + b, \quad \text{not} \quad -(a + b).$$

It is sheer luck that $-ab$ is not ambiguous in ordinary algebra; but in the algebra of statements, both

$$\sim p \wedge q \quad \text{and} \quad \sim p \vee q$$

are ambiguous. A good many parentheses can be avoided by the simple expedient of putting the negation sign above when it applies only to a single letter: thus we can write De Morgan's laws

$$\sim(p \wedge q) \equiv \tilde{p} \vee \tilde{q}, \qquad \sim(p \vee q) \equiv \tilde{p} \wedge \tilde{q}.$$

(There is no way to avoid the parentheses on the left until someone invents better typesetting equipment: $\overparen{p \wedge q}$ is easy to write, but if it is to be set in type it must be done by hand.)

One other convention will save a few parentheses. Let us suppose that unless held together by parentheses, any expression with an arrow (either one-way or two-way) "falls apart" at the arrow. Thus

$$p \wedge q \Rightarrow r \quad \text{represents} \quad (p \wedge q) \Rightarrow r, \quad \text{not} \quad p \wedge (q \Rightarrow r),$$
$$p \vee q \Rightarrow r \quad \text{represents} \quad (p \vee q) \Rightarrow r, \quad \text{not} \quad p \vee (q \Rightarrow r),$$

and similarly for the converses. (Of the four possibilities here, only $p \Rightarrow q \vee r$ is not ambiguous, because disjunction is associative.)

Note in particular that $p \Rightarrow q \Rightarrow r$ is quite illegal: implication is *not* associative,

$$p \Rightarrow (q \Rightarrow r) \equiv \tilde{p} \vee (\tilde{q} \vee r)$$
$$\equiv (\tilde{p} \vee \tilde{q}) \vee r,$$
$$(p \Rightarrow q) \Rightarrow r \equiv \sim(\tilde{p} \vee q) \vee r$$
$$\equiv (p \wedge \tilde{q}) \vee r$$

(with F for both p and r, we get T for the first and F for the second).

Although we require a special convention in order to drop the parentheses in

$$(p \wedge q) \Leftrightarrow (q \wedge p),$$

we need none for

$$(p \wedge q) \equiv (q \wedge p).$$

The first is a form, and thus is one of the things (namely forms) that we are discussing; the second is an assertion about a pair of those things. The difference between them is like that between a person (say, Sam) and some statement about two people (say, Sam is as old as Mary). Hence although

$$p \wedge q \Leftrightarrow q \wedge p$$

might conceivably represent any of

$$((p \wedge q) \Leftrightarrow q) \wedge p$$
$$p \wedge (q \Leftrightarrow q) \wedge p$$
$$(p \wedge q) \Leftrightarrow (q \wedge p)$$
$$p \wedge (q \Leftrightarrow (q \wedge p))$$

(our convention tells us it represents the third one),

$$p \wedge q \equiv q \wedge p$$

can only represent

$$(p \wedge q) \equiv (q \wedge p).$$

The other combinations must be considered gibberish on a par with

$$a + (b = c).$$

EXERCISES

1. Write truth tables for $p \Rightarrow q, q \Rightarrow p, \tilde{p} \Rightarrow p, p \Rightarrow \tilde{p}$.

2. Using truth tables, prove the following equivalences:
   (a) $p \Rightarrow q \equiv \tilde{q} \Rightarrow \tilde{p}$
   (b) $p \Rightarrow (q \Rightarrow r) \equiv q \Rightarrow (p \Rightarrow r)$
   (c) $p \Leftrightarrow q \equiv (p \wedge q) \vee (\tilde{p} \wedge \tilde{q})$.

3. Clearly $\Leftrightarrow$ is commutative: $p \Leftrightarrow q \equiv q \Leftrightarrow p$. Is it associative?

4. The forms $(p \wedge q) \vee r$ and $p \wedge (q \vee r)$ are *not* equivalent. Show, however, that one of them "tautologically implies" the other.

5. Express each of the sentences in Exercise 6 of Section 1 as either an implication or the negation of an implication, and give an English version for each of your symbolic expressions.

6. The equivalences

$$p \wedge q \equiv \sim(\tilde{p} \vee \tilde{q}),$$
$$p \Rightarrow q \equiv \tilde{p} \vee q,$$
$$p \Leftrightarrow q \equiv (p \Rightarrow q) \wedge (q \Rightarrow p)$$

show that the connectives $\wedge, \Rightarrow, \Leftrightarrow$ may all be expressed in terms of the two connectives $\sim, \vee$. We call $\sim, \vee$ a *basic pair* of connectives because all the others can be defined in terms of these two.

   (a) Express $p \Leftrightarrow q$ in terms of $\sim, \vee$ only.
   (b) Show that $\sim, \wedge$ is a basic pair.
   (c) Find another basic pair.

7. Define $p \downarrow q$ by the following table,

p	q	$p \downarrow q$
T	T	F
T	F	F
F	T	F
F	F	T

and establish the following equivalences:

(a) $\sim p \equiv p \downarrow p$
(b) $p \vee q \equiv (p \downarrow q) \downarrow (p \downarrow q)$
(c) $p \wedge q \equiv (p \downarrow p) \downarrow (q \downarrow q)$.

8. Define $p \uparrow q$ by the following table,

p	q	$p \uparrow q$
T	T	F
T	F	T
F	T	T
F	F	T

and express each of $\sim p$, $p \vee q$, $p \wedge q$ in terms of $\uparrow$ only.

4. ALGEBRAIC DERIVATION

In this section we examine the technique of "algebraic manipulation" in the algebra of statements. Later we shall apply it to the analysis of some verbal problems. The starting point for the algebraic work in this section is the list of "basic laws" discussed in Section 2. In Section 2, these laws were all established by reference to truth tables. One of our objects in this section is to enlarge the list of laws of the algebra of statements, and to do so without further reference to truth tables. Another is to get a great many tautologies. Truth tables provide a simple routine for deciding whether a given pair of compound forms are equivalent or whether a given form is a tautology, but they are not very efficient for the discovery of new equivalences and tautologies. Here we show how equivalences and tautologies may be derived from the basic laws using the sort of techniques one studies in elementary algebra.

A statement form A is a tautology if and only if $A \equiv I$. Thus establishing tautologies may be interpreted as proving equivalences having a certain special form. Conversely, any equivalence $A \equiv B$ may be established by proving that $A \Leftrightarrow B$ is a tautology. Our two problems are therefore equivalent since any method for deriving equivalences can be adapted to justify tautologies, and vice versa. In order to exploit the analogy with elementary algebra we concentrate first on equivalences.

Equivalences in the algebra of statements are the analogues of the identities in elementary algebra. Thus

$$(x - y)^2 = x^2 - 2xy + y^2$$

is an algebraic identity just because any replacement of the unknowns x, y by numerals converts the two sides into expressions for the same number.

Here it is to be understood that *each x* must be replaced by the same numeral; similarly for each of the unknowns in any identity. Let us say that a replacement of this kind is *uniform*. On the other hand,

$$\sim(p \lor q) \equiv (\sim p) \land (\sim q)$$

is an equivalence just because each uniform replacement of the symbols p, q by specific statements converts the two sides into compound statements having the same truth value.

For our algebra of statement forms we use a number of "derivation rules" which are exact analogues of the rules used in elementary algebra to derive identities.

Derivation Rules

If A is any statement form, it is equivalent to itself: $A \equiv A$. That is to say, equivalence is *reflexive*. Here is one easy way to get quite a few equivalences. There are some other ways which differ from this one because we begin with one or more equivalences and, from them, produce others.

Thus, for A and B any statement forms: given $A \equiv B$, we may assert $B \equiv A$. In words, equivalence is *symmetric*. It is *transitive* too. For A, B, and C any statement forms: given $A \equiv B$ and $B \equiv C$, we may assert $A \equiv C$.

Substitution. Given $A \equiv B$, we may assert

$$A \land C \equiv B \land C, \qquad A \lor C \equiv A \lor C, \qquad \sim A \equiv \sim B.$$

These last three rules are usually referred to as "substitution": they correspond to the algebraic maneuver of replacing one algebraic expression by another identically equal to the first, and then asserting that the two versions are identically equal. Their algebraic counterparts are often described either as "adding equals," "multiplying by equals," etc., or as "substituting equals for equals."

Specialization. There is another rule, quite different from the last three, which many writers call "substitution" too. It works as follows: Suppose that we know

$$(x + y)^2 = x^2 + 2xy + y^2$$

is an identity, and that we replace x and y uniformly by any algebraic expressions; then the result is also an identity. For example, writing $x + y$ in place of x, and z in place of y, we get

$$((x + y) + z)^2 = (x + y)^2 + 2(x + y)z + z^2,$$

which must be an identity because it is a "special case" of our given identity.

Similarly, given the equivalence

$$\sim(p \wedge q) \equiv (\sim p) \vee (\sim q)$$

and putting $p \vee q$ in place of p and $r \Rightarrow s$ in place of q, we get

$$\sim[(p \vee q) \wedge (r \Rightarrow s)] \equiv [\sim(p \vee q)] \vee [\sim(r \Rightarrow s)].$$

Here we are not obliged to construct truth tables (which, in this particular case, require 16 rows) in order to verify that what we have is an equivalence: it is sufficient to recognize that it is a special case of a known equivalence.

We turn now to a series of examples illustrating how the rules permit us to derive equivalences and tautologies from our basic list of equivalences given at the end of Section 2. In accordance with long established custom in writing algebraic derivations, we shall employ our derivation rules without feeling obliged to indicate which ones we use.

Example 1 Simplify $p \vee (\bar{p} \wedge q)$.

Solution:

$$
\begin{aligned}
p \vee (\bar{p} \wedge q) &\equiv (p \vee \bar{p}) \wedge (p \vee q) && \text{[Distr} \\
&\equiv I \wedge (p \vee q) && \text{[Comp} \\
&\equiv p \vee q && \text{[Ident}
\end{aligned}
$$

Example 2 Prove $(p \wedge \bar{q}) \vee q \equiv p \vee q$.

Solution:

$$
\begin{aligned}
(p \wedge \bar{q}) \vee q &\equiv q \vee (p \wedge \bar{q}) && \text{[Comm} \\
&\equiv q \vee (\bar{q} \wedge p) && \text{[Comm} \\
&\equiv q \vee p && \text{[Ex. 1 } (p \text{ for } q, q \text{ for } p) \\
&\equiv p \vee q && \text{[Comm}
\end{aligned}
$$

Example 3 Simplify $p \wedge (p \vee q)$.

Solution:

$$
\begin{aligned}
p \wedge (p \vee q) &\equiv (p \vee O) \wedge (p \vee q) && \text{[Ident} \\
&\equiv p \vee (O \wedge q) && \text{[Distr} \\
&\equiv p \vee O && \text{[Ident} \\
&\equiv p && \text{[Ident}
\end{aligned}
$$

Example 4 Simplify $p \Rightarrow \bar{p}$.

Solution:

$$
\begin{aligned}
p \Rightarrow \bar{p} &\equiv \bar{p} \vee \bar{p} && \text{[Def} \Rightarrow \\
&\equiv \bar{p} && \text{[Idem}
\end{aligned}
$$

Example 5 Show that $p \Rightarrow (p \lor q)$ is a tautology.

Solution:

$$
\begin{aligned}
p \Rightarrow (p \lor q) &\equiv \bar{p} \lor (p \lor q) && \text{[Def} \Rightarrow \\
&\equiv (\bar{p} \lor p) \lor q && \text{[Assoc} \\
&\equiv I \lor q && \text{[Comp} \\
&\equiv I && \text{[Ident}
\end{aligned}
$$

Example 6 Show that $p \land (p \Rightarrow q) \Rightarrow q$ is a tautology.

Solution:

$$
\begin{aligned}
p \land (p \Rightarrow q) \Rightarrow q &\equiv \sim[p \land (p \Rightarrow q)] \lor q && \text{[Def} \Rightarrow \\
&\equiv \sim[p \land (\bar{p} \lor q)] \lor q && \text{[Def} \Rightarrow \\
&\equiv [\bar{p} \lor (p \land \bar{q})] \lor q && \text{[De M, Inv} \\
&\equiv \bar{p} \lor [(p \land \bar{q}) \lor q] && \text{[Assoc} \\
&\equiv \bar{p} \lor (p \lor q) && \text{[Ex. 2} \\
&\equiv (\bar{p} \lor p) \lor q && \text{[Assoc} \\
&\equiv I \lor q && \text{[Comp} \\
&\equiv I && \text{[Ident}
\end{aligned}
$$

Example 7 Prove $p \Rightarrow q \equiv \bar{q} \Rightarrow \bar{p}$.

Solution:

$$
\begin{aligned}
p \Rightarrow q &\equiv \bar{p} \lor q && \text{[Def} \Rightarrow \\
&\equiv q \lor \bar{p} && \text{[Comm} \\
&\equiv \sim(\sim q) \lor \bar{p} && \text{[Inv} \\
&\equiv \bar{q} \Rightarrow \bar{p} && \text{[Def} \Rightarrow
\end{aligned}
$$

Up to this point our technique for handling equivalences and tautologies involving $\Rightarrow$ has been to eliminate the arrow by appealing to its definition. The resulting expressions, involving only $\sim$, $\land$, $\lor$ may then be manipulated using the basic laws. As we extend our body of laws and obtain a longer list to which we may appeal, this reduction will not always be necessary because we shall be able to appeal to equivalences involving $\Rightarrow$. An example of such a derivation is given at the end of this section.

For convenience of later reference, we collect a number of equivalences and tautologies. These lists include those established in the preceding examples as well as a number of others whose proofs are left as exercises.

EQUIVALENCES

1. $p \land (p \lor q) \equiv p$ \qquad (Absorption)
2. $p \lor (p \land q) \equiv p$ \qquad (Absorption)
3. $p \land (\bar{p} \lor q) \equiv p \land q$

4. $p \lor (\bar{p} \land q) \equiv p \lor q$

5. $p \Rightarrow q \equiv \bar{q} \Rightarrow \bar{p}$

6. $p \Rightarrow (q \Rightarrow r) \equiv p \land q \Rightarrow r$

7. $p \land q \Rightarrow r \equiv p \land \bar{r} \Rightarrow \bar{q}$

8. $p \Rightarrow q \land r \equiv (p \Rightarrow q) \land (p \Rightarrow r)$

9. $p \Rightarrow q \lor r \equiv (p \Rightarrow q) \lor (p \Rightarrow r)$

10. $p \land q \Rightarrow r \equiv (p \Rightarrow r) \lor (q \Rightarrow r)$

11. $p \lor q \Rightarrow r \equiv (p \Rightarrow r) \land (q \Rightarrow r)$

TAUTOLOGIES

1. $p \Rightarrow p$

2. $p \land q \Rightarrow p$

3. $p \Rightarrow p \lor q$

4. $p \land (p \Rightarrow q) \Rightarrow q$

5. $(p \Rightarrow q) \Rightarrow (p \Rightarrow q \lor r)$

6. $(p \Rightarrow q) \Rightarrow (p \land r \Rightarrow q)$

7. $(p \lor r \Rightarrow q) \Rightarrow (p \Rightarrow q)$

8. $(p \Rightarrow q \land r) \Rightarrow (p \Rightarrow q)$

9. $(p \Rightarrow q) \Rightarrow (p \land r \Rightarrow q \land r)$

10. $(p \Rightarrow q) \Rightarrow (p \lor r \Rightarrow q \lor r)$

11. $(p \Rightarrow q) \land (q \Rightarrow r) \Rightarrow (p \Rightarrow r)$

When we find occasion to refer to particular items in these lists we shall cite them as E-1, ..., E-11, T-1, ..., T-11. Those which have already been established in the examples are E-1, E-4, E-5, T-3, T-4. We provide one more example, showing how T-5 may be deduced from T-3 and E-9. The rest we leave as exercises.

Example 8 T-5.

$$(p \Rightarrow q) \Rightarrow (p \Rightarrow q \lor r)$$
$$\equiv (p \Rightarrow q) \Rightarrow (p \Rightarrow q) \lor (p \Rightarrow r) \qquad \text{[E-9}$$

Thus T-5 is equivalent to a special case of T-3: $p \Rightarrow (p \lor q)$ (we have $p \Rightarrow q$ in place of p, and $p \Rightarrow r$ in place of q).

EXERCISES

1. Complete the project begun in the text by proving all the equivalences E-1, ..., E-11 without resorting to truth tables.

2. Derive the following equivalence from the basic laws:

$$(p \wedge q) \vee (p \wedge r) \vee (q \wedge r) \equiv (p \vee q) \wedge (p \vee r) \wedge (q \vee r).$$

3. Prove each of the following equivalences:

(a) $p \wedge q \Leftrightarrow p \equiv p \Rightarrow q$
(b) $p \vee q \Leftrightarrow q \equiv p \Rightarrow q$
(c) $(p \Rightarrow q) \wedge q \Rightarrow p \equiv q \Rightarrow p.$

4. Using the involution and De Morgan laws, derive half of the remaining basic laws from the other half.

5. (a) Using E-5, show that T-3 is equivalent to a special case of T-2.
   (b) Write E-3 in the form

$$p \wedge (p \Rightarrow q) \equiv p \wedge q$$

   and, using this and E-6, show that T-4, T-6, T-8, and T-11 are all equivalent to special cases of T-3.
   (c) In T-5 and T-7, replace both hypothesis and conclusion by their contrapositives (E-5) and show that the resulting expressions are special cases of T-6 and T-8, respectively.
   (d) Rewrite T-9, using E-6 and, using the version of E-3 in part (b) above in the hypothesis, show that T-9 is equivalent to a special case of T-2.
   (e) Using E-5, show that T-10 is equivalent to a special case of T-9.

6. Derive the following equivalences from E-8, E-9, E-10, E-11:

$$[(p \Rightarrow q) \wedge (p \Rightarrow s)] \vee [(r \Rightarrow q) \wedge (r \Rightarrow s)] \equiv (p \wedge r) \Rightarrow (q \wedge s)$$
$$[(p \Rightarrow q) \vee (r \Rightarrow q)] \wedge [(p \Rightarrow s) \vee (r \Rightarrow s)] \equiv (p \wedge r) \Rightarrow (q \wedge s)$$
$$[(p \Rightarrow q) \vee (p \Rightarrow s)] \wedge [(r \Rightarrow q) \vee (r \Rightarrow s)] \equiv (p \vee r) \Rightarrow (q \vee s)$$
$$[(p \Rightarrow q) \wedge (r \Rightarrow q)] \vee [(p \Rightarrow s) \wedge (r \Rightarrow s)] \equiv (p \vee r) \Rightarrow (q \vee s).$$

7. Derive the following tautologies from equivalences in Exercise 6:

$$[(p \Rightarrow q) \wedge (r \Rightarrow s)] \Rightarrow [(p \wedge r) \Rightarrow (q \wedge s)],$$
$$[(p \Rightarrow q) \wedge (r \Rightarrow s)] \Rightarrow [(p \vee r) \Rightarrow (q \vee s)].$$

Tautologies T-9 and T-10 are special cases of these two.

8. Prove that three of the following are tautologies, and that one is not:

$$[(p \wedge r) \Rightarrow (q \vee s)] \Rightarrow [(p \Rightarrow q) \vee (r \Rightarrow s)]$$
$$[(p \Rightarrow q) \vee (r \Rightarrow s)] \Rightarrow [(p \wedge r) \Rightarrow (q \vee s)]$$
$$[(p \vee r) \Rightarrow (q \wedge s)] \Rightarrow [(p \Rightarrow q) \wedge (r \Rightarrow s)]$$
$$[(p \Rightarrow q) \wedge (r \Rightarrow s)] \Rightarrow [(p \vee r) \Rightarrow (q \wedge s)].$$

5. SOME APPLICATIONS

In this section and the next we study some problems which can be solved with our algebra of statements. Although there are important features common to all of them, they may be divided into two main classes: transformation and inference. The transformation problems, considered in this section, deal with the question of restating or rephrasing given compound statements. The equivalences of our algebra supply the means for doing this. Problems of inference involve drawing "conclusions" from given "premises," and rely on tautologies for their justification. We shall observe later that the transformation problems may be thought of as inference problems of a very special kind.

We begin our study of transformation problems by examining some "general" examples of compound statements, and then restrict our attention to a rather "special" class of statements occurring in some problems dealing with electrical networks. All that is "special" about the latter statements is the restriction of the subject of discourse.

Transformation

When the symbols appearing in an equivalence are uniformly replaced by specific statements, each "member" or "side" of the equivalence is converted into a compound statement. Suppose that A and B are equivalent forms and that A_0, B_0 are compound statements resulting respectively from the forms A, B when each symbol in the equivalence $A \equiv B$ is uniformly replaced by a letter representing a specific statement. Then it follows that A_0 and B_0, which we shall refer to as *instances* of A and B respectively, are either both true or both false.

For an example, consider the equivalence

$$p \lor (q \land r) \equiv (p \lor q) \land (p \lor r).$$

If a, b, c are any three specific statements, it follows that

$$a \lor (b \land c) \quad \text{and} \quad (a \lor b) \land (a \lor c)$$

have the same truth value, so neither can be true unless the other is too. For a specific example, take

a: *Virtue is its own reward.*

b: *Some scoundrels triumph.*

c: *Many good people suffer.*

Then $a \lor (b \land c)$ represents

Either virtue is its own reward, or some scoundrels triumph and many good people suffer.

On the other hand, $(a \lor b) \land (a \lor c)$ represents

Either virtue is its own reward or some scoundrels triumph, and either virtue is its own reward or many good people suffer.

This particular example, while it may be uplifting, is neither profound nor especially interesting: it does at least provide an illustration of the way an equivalence may be used to transform one compound statement into another.

The use of equivalences for such transformations is the exact analogue of the use of algebraic identities in arithmetical problems such as factorization:

$$63 = 64 - 1 = 8^2 - 1 = (8 - 1)(8 + 1) = 7(9),$$
$$1729 = 1728 + 1 = 12^3 + 1^3 = 13(12^2 - 12 + 1)$$
$$= 13(144 - 11) = 13(133),$$
$$1729 = 1000 + 729 = 10^3 + 9^3 = 19(10^2 - 10 \cdot 9 + 9^2)$$
$$= 19(10 + 81) = 19(91).$$

In the first example, we use the identity

$$x^2 - 1 = (x - 1)(x + 1);$$

for the other two, we obtain the factorizations from the identity

$$x^3 + y^3 = (x + y)(x^2 - xy + y^2).$$

Hans Reichenbach is responsible for the following example.* Consider the statement

It is not the case that Cleopatra was alive in 1938 and was not married to Hitler and not to Mussolini.

Introduce the following notation:

a: *Cleopatra was alive in 1938.*

b: *Cleopatra was married to Hitler.*

c: *Cleopatra was married to Mussolini*

Then the statement may be written

$$\sim[a \wedge (\sim b) \wedge (\sim c)].$$

Transforming by one of De Morgan's laws,

$$\bar{a} \vee b \vee c,$$

and using the definition for $\Rightarrow$, we have

$$a \Rightarrow b \vee c.$$

Thus the original statement may be considered a roundabout way of asserting

If Cleopatra was alive in 1938, then she was married to Hitler or to Mussolini (or both).

---

* *Elements of Symbolic Logic*, Macmillan, New York, 1947.

This example illustrates how the algebra of statements may be used to decode complicated statements, a process sometimes useful for reading "small print" or advertising copy. This decoding is the analogue of "simplification" in ordinary algebra. On the other hand, our algebra of statements is equally useful for encoding (the analogue of algebraic "complication"). We leave for the reader any applications to politics, and turn instead to an engineering problem.

EXERCISES

Introduce letters to represent the components of each of the following compound statements and, using them, write an expression for the compound statement. Then use the basic laws and the equivalences in Section 4 to simplify your expression "as much as possible." Finally, translate the result into English.

1. If you drink, don't drive; [and] if you drive, don't drink.

2. Crime doesn't pay if either virtue is its own reward or crime doesn't pay.

3. If the team must win in order to avoid bankruptcy, then it will go bankrupt.

4. If a woman is neither vain nor fickle, then it does not follow that she would be beautiful if she were vain.

5. A man gains a tax exemption if he marries, but he lives to regret it if he marries and does not gain a tax exemption.

6. Either a man gets a tax exemption when he marries, or he lives to regret it if he marries and does not get a tax exemption.

7. If a man marries he gets a tax exemption, but he lives to regret it if he gets a tax exemption when he marries.

8. If either Mozart was a genius, or Haydn was prolific if Handel was profound, it follows that Bach was a giant if Mozart was a genius.

9. It is either the case that Pythagoras was fallible if Plato was no dunce, or that Pythagoras was fallible if either Plato was a dunce or numerology is not profound.

10. Assuming that matter is not made of atoms if there are only four elements, it follows that matter is made of atoms if we are to believe Democritus.

11. If Media was jealous, then not only were her children doomed but Jason would have had a problem on his hands even if Medea were not jealous.

12. If the assumption that Augustus was an emperor implies that he was neither a god nor an emperor, then the assumption that he was not an emperor implies both that he was an emperor and that his mother was mad.

13. The assumption that either Philip of Macedon was the father of his country, or that it does not follow that he was a local despot if he was the father of his country, implies that he was the father of his country and that Alexander the Great was Cleopatra's uncle.

14. If the assertion that this book follows CUPM recommendations implies that it is endorsed by CUPM, then the assertion that it does not follow CUPM recommendations does not imply that it is endorsed by CUPM.

Switching Networks

Switches are used to "open" and "close" electric circuits and may be indicated schematically as follows:

Open switch   Closed switch

When a switch is open it prevents "current" from passing; when it is closed it "conducts." Two or more switches may be wired together in a variety of ways. For example, two switches on the same line

Two switches in series

are said to be in *series*: a series connection will carry current if and only if both switches are closed. Two switches on alternate lines

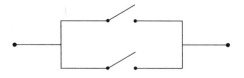

Two switches in parallel

are said to be in *parallel*: a parallel connection will conduct if and only if at least one of the switches is closed. The "ends of the line," indicated by large dots in these drawings, are called *terminals*. Our algebra of statements can be used to solve some of the problems arising in connection with so-called *two-terminal series-parallel networks*. We shall see that these problems are, apart from special terminology, identical to the transformation problems we studied.

The key ideas we exploit here are that a series connection can be described by a conjunction and a parallel connection by a disjunction. Suppose first that we have a circuit with just two switches. Give them names, say A and B. Let a be the statement A *is closed* and b the statement B *is closed*. If A and B are connected in series, then $a \wedge b$ asserts that the circuit is closed.

If A and B are connected in parallel, $a \vee b$ asserts that the circuit is closed.

Series: $a \wedge b$

Parallel: $a \vee b$

More complicated circuits may be analyzed by breaking them down into smaller parts. Thus

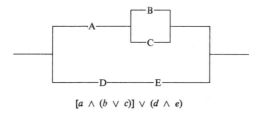

$[a \wedge (b \vee c)] \vee (d \wedge e)$

There are such things as "double-pole" and "triple-pole" switches, etc. These have more than one "arm" and are used to close two or more connections at once:

Double-pole

Triple-pole

Using multiple-pole switches, we can build networks like the following one requiring a pair (A, B) of double-pole switches and a pair (C, D) of "single-pole" switches:

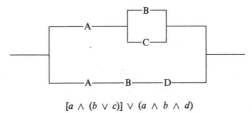

$[a \wedge (b \vee c)] \vee (a \wedge b \wedge d)$

This example, incidentally, is ridiculously complicated, as we may prove with our algebra. Using logical equivalences, we simplify the compound statement describing this network as follows:

$$[a \wedge (b \vee c)] \vee (a \wedge b \wedge d)$$
$$a \wedge [(b \vee c) \vee (b \wedge d)] \qquad \text{[Distr}$$
$$a \wedge \{c \vee [b \vee (b \wedge d)]\} \qquad \text{[Comm Assoc}$$
$$a \wedge (c \vee b) \qquad\qquad\quad \text{[Absorption}$$

The given network is therefore equivalent to the following one which requires only three of the less expensive single-pole switches:

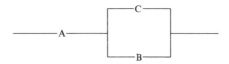

One final complication of the "hardware": there are so-called "double-throw" switches having "back contacts." We may illustrate them by such drawings as

A closed, A′ open   A open, A′ closed

When A opens a spring pulls the arm over and closes the contact at A′; A′ is called a *back contact* of switch A. Since A′ is closed if and only if A is open, $\bar{a}$ represents A′ *is closed* if a represents A *is closed*. Multiple-pole switches also come in deluxe models having back contacts. Either of the following circuits,

$(a \wedge b) \vee (\bar{a} \wedge \bar{b})$ $\qquad\qquad\qquad\qquad$ $(a \wedge \bar{b}) \vee (\bar{a} \wedge b)$

each requiring a pair of double-throw single-pole switches, may be used to operate a light independently from either of two stations. Such circuits could be used, for example, to operate a garage light if it is to be turned either on or off in the house or in the garage, or for a hall light which can be operated from either end of the hall. The first circuit conducts if both switches are "on," or if both are "off," and does not conduct if only one is "on" and the other is "off": thus throwing either switch changes the "state" of the circuit. The second circuit, which is the "negation" of the first, performs the same job just as well. In the first case the circuit conducts if the number of switches in the "on" position is even (0 or 2) and does not if the number is odd (that is, 1). For the other circuit it is the other way around.

We give an example to illustrate the "synthesis" and "simplification" involved in circuit design. Suppose a three-man committee requires a device to indicate majority votes: a light or buzzer to be operated if at least two members close the switches they control. The possibilities to be covered are represented by the following expression

$$(a \wedge b \wedge c) \vee (\bar{a} \wedge b \wedge c) \vee (a \wedge \bar{b} \wedge c) \vee (a \wedge b \wedge \bar{c})$$

and the corresponding circuit

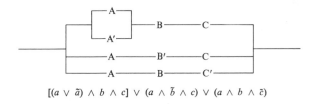

The upper branch of the circuit corresponds to unanimity, the others take account of the possible dissents permitted. As drawn, the circuit is quite extravagant: it requires three triple-pole double-throw switches. A great deal of simplification is possible. For example

$$[(a \vee \bar{a}) \wedge b \wedge c] \vee (a \wedge \bar{b} \wedge c) \vee (a \wedge b \wedge \bar{c})$$

or

$$(b \wedge c) \vee (a \wedge \bar{b} \wedge c) \vee (a \wedge b \wedge \bar{c}).$$

Simplifying further, we have

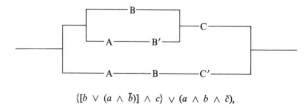

$$\{[b \lor (a \land \bar{b})] \land c\} \lor (a \land b \land \bar{c}),$$

and, with $b \lor a$ for $b \lor (a \land \bar{b})$, cf. E-4, we get

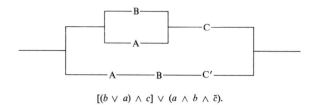

$$[(b \lor a) \land c] \lor (a \land b \land \bar{c}).$$

Rewriting,

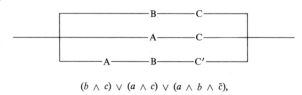

$$(b \land c) \lor (a \land c) \lor (a \land b \land \bar{c}),$$

we can work on the lower branches,

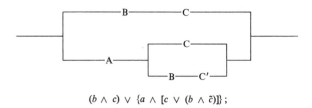

$$(b \land c) \lor \{a \land [c \lor (b \land \bar{c})]\} ;$$

and finally we eliminate the last back contact:

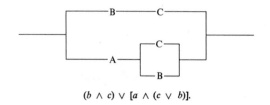

$$(b \land c) \lor [a \land (c \lor b)].$$

We have "boiled it down" to a circuit which requires one single-throw single-pole switch and two double-pole single-throw switches, and is consequently far more economical than our original design.

For our discussion of these problems we have used the terminology of switches. We could as well have spoken of "relays" which are merely switches operated by electric current instead of manual action, or of so-called "flip-flop" circuits which perform the same function electronically with vacuum tubes or transistors. The latter constitute some of the fundamental hardware of modern electronic calculating devices.

There is more to some of these problems than we have bothered to mention, and to that extent we have again been dealing with an abstraction rather than with the real thing. For one thing, we have ignored the physics of current flow. If you open a switch in a "hot" circuit (for example, if you pull a plug or blow a fuse), the current does not immediately jump to zero; it falls gradually to zero (rather rapidly, to be sure). The reverse happens when a switch is closed in a hot circuit: the current builds up to its "steady-state" value. In some complicated circuits such "transient" currents can cause trouble. [*Moral:* If you experiment with these things, don't connect your power supply until you have all the switches set. Better yet, learn some physics before you even try.]

EXERCISES

1. Imagine a committee of four which requires a majority to pass a motion, provided the chairman concurs (veto power). Design a circuit to indicate whether a motion passes.

2. Design a circuit to play the game of "matching pennies": Each of the players *A*, *B* controls a switch, which he may close or may not close. Have the circuit close if *A* wins.

3. Design as simple a circuit as you can to operate a light independently from each of three stations.

4. The circuits

are examples of so-called "bridges." They may be represented by compound statements obtained simply by enumerating all possible paths from one terminal to the other. Thus, for the first,

$$(b \land c) \lor (b \land a \land b) \lor (c \land b) \lor (c \land a \land c).$$

For each of these bridges, construct equivalent series-parallel circuits and simplify them as much as you can. Decide in each case whether the resulting circuit is or is not more "economical" than the bridge.

5. *Binary Adding Machine.* Using relays (for example), one can design circuits for a machine to add two (or more) numbers written in binary notation. For each "place" use two circuits, one for the "sum" S, the other for any "carry" to the next place. Consider two numbers and let A, B represent their bits (= binary "digits") in a given place, with C for the bit carried to that place and C^* for the bit carried to the next place. Suppose bit 1 is represented by a closed switch and 0 by an open switch. The addition rules are given in the accompanying table.

A	B	C	S	C^*
1	1	1	1	1
1	1	0	0	1
1	0	1	0	1
1	0	0	1	0
0	1	1	0	1
0	1	0	1	0
0	0	1	1	0
0	0	0	0	0

(Here S is 1 if an odd number of A, B, C are 1, and C^* is 1 if at least two of A, B, C are 1.) Thus, for the "sum" and "carry" circuits, we have

S: $(a \land b \land c) \lor (a \land \tilde{b} \land \tilde{c}) \lor (\tilde{a} \land b \land \tilde{c}) \lor (\tilde{a} \land \tilde{b} \land c)$,
C^*: $(a \land b \land c) \lor (a \land b \land \tilde{c}) \lor (a \land \tilde{b} \land c) \lor (\tilde{a} \land b \land c)$.

"Simplify" these circuits as much as you can.

6. Prove that the following two circuits are equivalent.

7. Construct the "negations" of the following circuits and prove that they are equivalent.

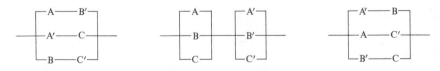

8. Prove that both of the following circuits are equivalent to the three circuits drawn in Exercise 7.

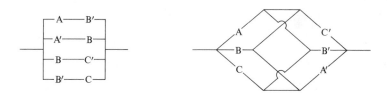

6. INFERENCE

We now consider an important type of problem: inference, the drawing of "conclusions" from given "premises." As we shall observe shortly, the transformation problems discussed in the last section represent special cases of the more general kind of problems we now consider.

The process of inference is fundamental in mathematics and, indeed, in every discipline in which careful reasoning has a place: all deductive arguments, including mathematical proofs, are "chains" of inferences. We supplement our discussion of inferences with a brief examination of fallacies and indicate how some alleged proofs may be either justified or exposed as frauds.

Here our attention is necessarily restricted to things we may do with statements as wholes. We have already observed that our theory up to this point is not elaborate enough to permit us to describe some of the simplest mathematical theorems. It must then be granted that we are not yet in a position to discuss what it takes to prove one of them. This section is only an introduction to the more refined ideas we shall encounter later.

The theory of inference discussed in this section may seem at first to be rather naive. It is not. In Chapter 2 we shall encounter some fairly involved proofs in the "algebra of sets." We shall find, however, that the proofs in Chapter 2 can be analyzed completely using only the "naive" theory of inference developed in this section. In Chapter 3 we discuss sentence structure. There we shall see that our original theory of inference can be carried over intact, once we have more sophisticated tautologies at our disposal.

If A and B are forms and $A \Rightarrow B$ is a tautology, we call $A \Rightarrow B$ a *tautological implication*. If the symbols in a tautological implication are uniformly replaced by specific statements, we know of course that the resulting compound statement, say $A_0 \Rightarrow B_0$, is true. But we can say much more. A glance at the truth table for $\Rightarrow$ shows that *in case* the statement A_0 happens to be true when $A_0 \Rightarrow B_0$ is true, it must also be the case that B_0 is true. We express this fact by saying that B_0 may be *deduced*, or *inferred*, from A_0. In particular, if A_0 is the conjunction of several statements $A_1, A_2, \ldots, A_n$, we say that B_0 may be inferred from $A_1, A_2, \ldots, A_n$. B_0 is called the *conclusion* while A_0 or $A_1, A_2, \ldots, A_n$ are called the *premises* of the inference. We shall indicate this relation schematically by writing $A_0 \therefore B_0$, or $A_1, A_2, \ldots, A_n \therefore B_0$, and by quoting or citing the pertinent tautology.

We have at hand a generous fund of tautological implications. There are those listed in Section 4 and there are others scattered throughout the collections of exercises in this chapter. In addition, we get two more from each basic law and from each of the other equivalences of our algebra: for if $A \equiv B$ represents any equivalence of forms, then each of the compound forms

$$A \Rightarrow B, \qquad B \Rightarrow A$$

is a tautological implication.

We illustrate the process of inference with a very simple example. Consider the single compound premise

> *You can fool all the people some of the time, and some of the people all the time, but you cannot fool all the people all of the time.*

We write this in the form $a \wedge b \wedge c$ and from this premise we may infer

a: *You can fool all the people some of the time.*

The reason we may draw this conclusion is that

$$a \wedge b \wedge c \Rightarrow a$$

is an instance of tautology T-2: $p \wedge q \Rightarrow p$. Schematically,

$$a \wedge b \wedge c \therefore a \qquad [p \wedge q \Rightarrow p,$$

or

$$a, b, c \therefore a \qquad [p \wedge q \Rightarrow p.$$

One point cannot be overemphasized. Our justification for drawing a conclusion, as we just did in our simple example, has nothing whatever to do with whether or not any of the premises or the conclusion is true. The whole business of drawing conclusion B_0 from premise A_0 hinges on whether the compound statement $A_0 \Rightarrow B_0$ is an instance of a tautology; no other consideration is relevant.

As the example clearly shows, something was lost in the process of inference: the conclusion asserts a good deal less than the premise does. Although this need not happen in certain "exceptional" cases, it is fairly typical. This loss may be accounted for by observing that although $p \wedge q \Rightarrow p$ is a tautology, $p \Rightarrow p \wedge q$ is not. Suppose, however, that both $A \Rightarrow B$ and $B \Rightarrow A$ are tautological implications, in which case it follows that A and B are equivalent forms. Then an inference based on the tautology $A \Rightarrow B$ results in a conclusion having the same "force" as the premise, since we have at hand another tautology, $B \Rightarrow A$, with which we may "infer" the "premise" from the "conclusion." The latter situation has already been examined, it is the problem of transformation: replacing one statement by another, the pair standing or falling together. These observations justify our claim that transformation is a special case of inference. Inferences are based on tautologies of the form $A \Rightarrow B$; transformations are inferences based on tautological implications having the more restricted form $A \Leftrightarrow B$.

Our first example was rather trivial: the conclusion we drew was part of the premise, or was itself one of the premises, depending on how one chooses to analyze it. There are examples which are somewhat less trivial. Consider the pair of premises

(1) *Good steaks are expensive.*

(2) *If good steaks are expensive, not everyone can afford to buy good steaks.*

Suppose we write a for the first premise and $a \Rightarrow b$ for the second. We are entitled to replace our pair of premises by the single compound premise $a \wedge (a \Rightarrow b)$, and from the latter we may infer b as a conclusion, since

$$a \wedge (a \Rightarrow b) \Rightarrow b$$

is an instance of tautology T-4: $p \wedge (p \Rightarrow q) \Rightarrow q$. Schematically,

$$a, \, a \Rightarrow b \, \therefore \, b \qquad \text{[T-4.}$$

From the premises

(1) *If man is a rational animal, then there is some hope for the human race.*

(2) *If there is some hope for the human race, then women have a place in the world.*

we may infer

If man is a rational animal, then women have a place in the world.

The justification is this: from premises of the form $a \Rightarrow b$ and $b \Rightarrow c$, we may infer $a \Rightarrow c$, since

$$(a \Rightarrow b) \wedge (b \Rightarrow c) \Rightarrow (a \Rightarrow c)$$

is an instance of tautology T-11:

$$(p \Rightarrow q) \wedge (q \Rightarrow r) \Rightarrow (p \Rightarrow r).$$

We emphasize again that whether or not any of the premises or the conclusion are true is quite irrelevant as far as our ability to draw the conclusion is concerned. We may say, of course, that in case all the premises should happen to be true, then we are assured that the conclusion must be true as well. (In our last example, this turns out to be the case if, *inter alia*, the melancholy facts of life should be that all three of the statements a, b, c are false, for then $a \Rightarrow b$ and $b \Rightarrow c$ are both true.)

We have claimed that our second and third examples are "somewhat less trivial" than our first. This opinion is disputable; certainly they are not much less trivial. The fact of the matter is that all examples really are quite trivial. Inference cannot "add" something to what is already "there" in the premises, it merely enables us to shuffle or to rearrange what is given or to pluck out one of the several statements from which the premises are constructed. For all that, inference is not to be deprecated: a mathematical proof is nothing but a more or less complicated chain of inferences. The links may not amount to much in their own right, but such chains can accomplish mighty feats.

By a *chain of inferences* from a given collection of premises we mean several inferences arranged in a definite order and so related that every premise of each inference is either one of the given premises or is the conclusion of one of the preceding inferences. We give an example.

> *When the sands are all dry, he is gay as a lark,*
> *And will talk in contemptuous tones of the Shark:*
> *But, when the tide rises and sharks are around,*
> *His voice has a timid and tremulous sound.*

We assume, as a third premise, that he (the Lobster, incidentally) will not talk in contemptuous tones of the Shark if his voice has a timid and tremulous sound, and deduce that the sands are not all dry when the tide rises and sharks are around. With the following notation

a: *The sands are all dry.*

b: *He is gay as a lark.*

c: *He will talk in contemptuous tones of the Shark.*

d: *The tide rises.*

e: *Sharks are around.*

f: *His voice has a timid and tremulous sound.*

our premises are

$$(1)\ a \Rightarrow b \wedge c$$
$$(2)\ d \wedge e \Rightarrow f$$
$$(3)\ f \Rightarrow \tilde{c}.$$

We construct a chain of four inferences:

$$(\mathrm{I})\quad d \wedge e \Rightarrow f,\ f \Rightarrow \tilde{c} \therefore d \wedge e \Rightarrow \tilde{c} \qquad [\text{T-11}$$
$$(\mathrm{II})\quad a \Rightarrow b \wedge c \therefore a \Rightarrow c \qquad [\text{T-8}$$
$$(\mathrm{III})\quad a \Rightarrow c \therefore \tilde{c} \Rightarrow \tilde{a} \qquad [\text{E-5}$$
$$(\mathrm{IV})\quad d \wedge e \Rightarrow \tilde{c},\ \tilde{c} \Rightarrow \tilde{a} \therefore d \wedge e \Rightarrow \tilde{a} \qquad [\text{T-11}$$

Of these, (I) and (II) use the given premises. The premise for (III) is the conclusion of (II) and the premises for (IV) are the conclusions of (I) and (III).

Many problems of this kind can be simplified by a "trick." If the conclusion has the form $a \Rightarrow b$, the inference pattern is

$$A_0 \mathrel{\therefore} a \Rightarrow b,$$

where A_0 is the conjunction of the premises. Now the tautology validating the inference must be

$$A \Rightarrow (p \Rightarrow q),$$

where A is a statement form with A_0 as an instance. But in view of E-6, $A \Rightarrow (p \Rightarrow q)$ and $A \wedge p \Rightarrow q$ are equivalent; so either of these forms is a tautology if the other is. Thus the inference $A_0 \mathrel{\therefore} a \Rightarrow b$ is "equivalent" to the inference $A_0, a \mathrel{\therefore} b$. Usually the latter is the easier to carry out, for more is "assumed" and less is to be "deduced." We call this ruse "assuming the hypothesis": it is well known among students of elementary synthetic geometry. A variation on the same theme ("denying the conclusion") is popular in indirect proofs: instead of $A_0 \mathrel{\therefore} a \Rightarrow b$ one seeks to show $A_0 \mathrel{\therefore} \tilde{b} \Rightarrow \tilde{a}$ which, in turn, is attacked in the form $A_0, \tilde{b} \mathrel{\therefore} \tilde{a}$.

The recognition that the inferences

$$A_0, a \mathrel{\therefore} b \qquad \text{and} \qquad A_0, \tilde{b} \mathrel{\therefore} \tilde{a}$$

are equivalent goes back to ancient times and plays an important role in the theory of "syllogisms," as we shall see in Chapter 3. This particular method of transforming one inference pattern into another we shall call *contraposition*.

EXERCISES

Justify each of the inferences by constructing chains which invoke tautologies established in the text or left as exercises. (In a number of these exercises, the work will be simplified if some of the premises and intermediate conclusions are transformed using equivalences before they are combined with other statements to construct inferences.)

1. *Premises:* If rhubarb is edible, cabbage is delicious. Either rhubarb is edible, or mustard greens are rabbit food. If mustard greens are rabbit food, then sunflower seeds are not for the birds. Sunflower seeds are for the birds.

   Conclusion: Cabbage is delicious.

2. *Premises:* If Euclid was great, Archimedes was the greatest of all. Euclid's greatness is not grounds for denying that Thales invented geometry. If Thales invented geometry, then Eudoxus was second to one only.

   Conclusion: Eudoxus was second to one only, but Archimedes was the greatest of all.

3. *Premises:* French is easy if history is hard or German is complicated. If French is easy, then either chemistry is time-consuming or physics is impossible.

   Conclusion: If German is complicated and chemistry is not time-consuming, then physics is impossible.

4. *Premises:* Watson forgot his revolver if Holmes has his pipe. If Lestrade is confused, the game is afoot and Watson remembered his revolver. If Holmes is alert, then either Lestrade is confused or Holmes has his pipe.

   Conclusion: If Holmes is alert and Watson remembered his revolver, the game is afoot.

5. *Premises:* If there are four cardinal virtues and charity is not the greatest of the other three, then faith and fortitude are no stronger than prudence and hope. If either there are four cardinal virtues or charity is not the greatest of the other three, then justice and moderation are compatible. But if faith and fortitude are no stronger than prudence and hope, then justice and moderation are incompatible.

   Conclusion: If there are four cardinal virtues, then charity is the greatest of the other three.

6. *Premises:* If Pride is the greatest of the sins, then either Avarice and Envy support each other or Lechery and Sloth are a curious combination. If Lechery and Sloth are a curious combination, then either Anger and Gluttony are in classes by themselves or Envy is not the least of the sins. If Avarice and Envy support each other, then Pride is not the greatest of the sins; but Envy is not the least of the sins if Anger and Gluttony are in classes by themselves.

   Conclusion: If Pride is the greatest of the sins, Envy is not the least.

7. *Premises:* If joy reigns, there is no sorrow. When connivance thrives, there is either sorrow or heartbreak. If the police fail to act, either connivance thrives or chicanery flourishes. There can be no heartbreak without sorrow.

   Conclusion: When the police fail to act, chicanery flourishes if joy reigns.

8. *Premises:* If either Napoleon outfought everybody or Waterloo didn't really count, then either Wellington didn't win or Nelson wasn't around. Assuming that Napoleon held Moscow if history is a pack of lies, it follows that Napoleon outfought everybody. But, if Napoleon didn't hold Moscow, and if Waterloo did really count, then history is not a pack of lies.

   Conclusion: Nelson wasn't around if Wellington won.

9. *Premises:* If either Napoleon outfought everybody or Waterloo didn't really count, then either Wellington didn't win or Nelson wasn't around. Assuming that Napoleon held Moscow if history is a pack of lies, it follows that Napoleon outfought everybody. But, if Napoleon didn't hold Moscow, or if Waterloo did really count, then history is not a pack of lies.

   Conclusion: Nelson wasn't around if Wellington won.

Fallacies

The essential ingredients of an inference are some premises, a conclusion, and a tautology. The tautology provides the link between premises and conclusion and is what holds the whole thing together. We have discussed the nature of that link in some detail. We now consider *fallacies*: discussions occasionally mistaken for inferences, but defective in some respect.

The innocence, or the cunning, responsible for the existence of fallacies, and the credulity on which their success depends must surely inspire awe in even the most casual student of human nature. Indeed, people seem disposed to believe what they want to believe, no matter what reasons there may be, if any, pro or con. So fundamental is the urge that a major industry flourishes by exploiting it to sell goods and services, national policies are promulgated with the techniques of propaganda, and rumor has it that some politicians are anxious to say anything if they think it will gain them more votes than it will lose. In particular, mankind appears doomed to inundation by pseudo-inferences. The situation is so bad that many writers speak of *valid inference* for what we have called *inference*, and apparently find the use of the modifier neither redundant nor pretentious.

No one with much regard for human ingenuity could imagine it possible to compile a catalog of fallacious arguments that would do justice to the subject. We shall merely look at one or two examples of fallacies and indicate tests by which they may be exposed. We are concerned with conclusions "drawn" from inadequate premises and, in particular, we ignore such gems as statements which do not assert what the reader is expected to think they assert (*Satisfaction guaranteed or your money refunded*) and claims which are simply ambiguous (*Guaranteed used cars*).

Consider as premises

(1) *Technical education deserves generous financial support only if our engineers should be encouraged to build better rockets.*

(2) *Our engineers should be encouraged to build better rockets.*

and as conclusion

Technical education deserves generous financial support.

This is an example of what is very likely the most popular and overworked of all fallacies. Before we examine what is fallacious about it, we take the liberty of indicating some aspects of this example which are completely irrelevant to the problem we face. We are not at all concerned with such questions as whether any of the ideas mentioned in the premises or conclusion are noble, patriotic, misleading, or even deserving of consideration. We are not even concerned with whether or not any of the statements involved are true. The whole question, as we have repeatedly emphasized when discussing so-called valid inferences, is whether a presumption that the premises be true can force the conclusion to be true. Schematically, we have

$$a \Rightarrow b, \ b \therefore a.$$

This "inference" would be "valid" if

$$(a \Rightarrow b) \land b \Rightarrow a$$

were an instance of a tautology. As a matter of fact it is not:

$$(p \Rightarrow q) \land q \Rightarrow p \equiv q \Rightarrow p;$$

the form $(p \Rightarrow q) \land q \Rightarrow p$ has F in its truth table in the row in which p, q have respectively F, T.

A fallacy like this one may be exposed by giving a counterexample: by replacing the statements from which the premises and conclusion are constructed by other statements in such a way that the new "premises" are all true while the new "conclusion" is not. The idea behind this trick is that one instance represents a "valid" inference if and only if every instance does. We may modify the example above by taking

$$a: \quad 1 = 2,$$
$$b: \quad 1 + 2 = 2 + 1.$$

With these choices b is certainly true, and so is $a \Rightarrow b$ [Proof: If $1 = 2$, then $2 = 1$, because equality is symmetric; hence $1 + 2 = 2 + 1$, adding equals]. Each premise is therefore true. The "conclusion" a, however, is false.

Our analysis of the example shows not only what is wrong with it, but how it may be "patched up." Instead of appealing to a *bona fide* tautology, as a "valid" inference must, it invoked a nontautologous form equivalent to $q \Rightarrow p$. Since this is all we need, we may simply add as an extra premise the required instance $b \Rightarrow a$. (To the same end, it is simpler merely to delete the word *only* in the first premise.) Although a fallacy can often be patched up, it may not always be clear that in the process it will not lose sales or votes, or grades or whatever else is at stake.

This very fallacy $(a \Rightarrow b, b \therefore a)$ has had a long and glorious career in elementary mathematics. Anyone who "proves" an identity by showing that it implies $0 = 0$, or some more complicated instance of the formula $x = x$, is subscribing to the fallacy unless he takes pains to prove the converse: $0 = 0$ implies the identity in question.

For example, one might find something like the following three lines represented as a proof of the identity in line one:

$$(x + y)^3 = x^3 + 3xy^2 + 3x^2y + y^3,$$
$$(x + y)^2(x + y) = x^2(x + y) + 2xy(x + y) + y^2(x + y),$$
$$(x^2 + 2xy + y^2)(x + y) = (x^2 + 2xy + y^2)(x + y).$$

These three lines certainly meet the requirements for an algebraic derivation: each line is clearly a consequence of its predecessor, and that is exactly what is meant by putting one line below another in such a derivation. This derivation therefore shows that line three follows from line one; i.e.; line three is an identity if line one is an identity. Moreover, line three is clearly an identity, because equality is reflexive.

To conclude that the derivation above proves that line one is an identity is fallacious: the pattern for the "inference" being $a \Rightarrow b$, $b \therefore a$.

A *proof* is a finite sequence of assertions, *each* of which is some previously established result, one of the assumptions needed for the argument, or a consequence of one or more of its predecessors; the *last* of these assertions is whatever it is that the proof proves. From this point of view the three lines above show only that the last line, whose validity is clear on much simpler grounds, follows from the formula in line one. But the validity of the formula in line one must be in doubt or there would be no question of proving it. Thus our derivation is quite defective: not only does it not prove that line one is an identity; it doesn't even prove that line three is an identity.

We can patch up the proof by deriving line one from line three. This can be accomplished, in this case, quite easily: reverse the order in which the lines are written (3, 2, 1 for 1, 2, 3), or leave them where they are and stick the word *if* at the beginning of each line but the first. The reason such a simple trick is possible in this example is that each step of the original argument can be reversed. That line two follows from line one is irrelevant: what is important is that line one follows from line two. Similarly for lines two and three.

There are some who seek to avoid this fallacy by omitting the signs of equality in such derivations. Obviously there is no fallacy if nothing whatever is actually asserted, but there is no proof either. Decapitation, although marvelously effective, cannot be recommended as a cure for headaches.

In a sound argument each step can be justified; the details of a justification are often only sketched, and are omitted entirely when it is presumed the reader can supply them for himself. Because the "validity" of an argument is determined by examining such details, the novice may be at a disadvantage. In fact, it takes some practice to learn to tell a proof from a nonproof: one ought to be able to fill in the logical details, though confidence in one's ability to do it usually suffices.

A case can be made for the position that it is not the argument "itself" that is valid or fallacious, but rather what one takes for its justification. Consider, for example, the premises

> *Socrates is Greek.*
>
> *All Greeks are mortal.*

and the conclusion

> *Socrates is mortal.*

This argument cannot be justified by methods of this chapter, since $p \wedge q \Rightarrow r$ is not a tautology. About the most we can legitimately infer at this point about Socrates is that he is Greek. For problems like this one we need other tautologies. We shall get them in Chapter 3.

EXERCISES

1. Wherever there is smoke there is also fire or light. Wherever there is light or smoke there is also fire. There is no fire without either smoke or light. There is smoke here. What can you infer as to fire and light here?

2. Consider the three statements in Exercises 5, 6, and 7, page 29. Which ones, if any, can be inferred from one of the others?

CHAPTER TWO

ALGEBRA OF SETS

One may speak of a *class of students*, a *collection of gowns*, a *pack of thieves*, or an *association of alumni*. Each of these things is an example of what we call a *set*. The students, the gowns, the thieves, or the alumni, are said to *be members of, belong to*, or *be in*, the class, collection, pack, or association. Abstracting from these examples, and many others similar to them, we think of a "set" as a "collection" of "members." Everyday language is well supplied with words designating sets of one kind or other: *aggregate, alliance, anthology, army, arsenal, assembly, band, bevy, bloc, board*, (student) *body, brace, brood, bunch, cabinet, catalog, club, cohort, college, commission, committee, company*, (football) *conference, corps, couple, covey, crew, crowd*, and so on—right through the *alphabet*.

There are some sets whose members are themselves sets: for example, an association of learned societies or a council of pressure groups. Generally speaking, sets are treated as being on a "level of abstraction" distinct from that of their members. The members of a baseball team are men; one team cannot be a member of another. Teams are members of leagues.

We shall consider the words *set, class, collection* as synonyms and use them interchangeably. We shall often refer to a *member* of a set as an *element* of the set. We shall say that its members *belong to, are elements of*, or *lie in* the set. We also express the relation between an element and a set to which it belongs by writing

$$a \in A.$$

Here a is an element and A is a set; $\in$ stands for *is a member of, is an element of, belongs to*, etc. Thus if L is the set of points on a given line and p is a point, we write $p \in L$ to indicate that p lies on the line. We write $p \notin L$ to indicate that p does not lie on the line.

We offer formal definitions for none of the terms or expressions italicized in the previous paragraph. They are some of our undefined terms for this chapter. The purpose of the preceding paragraph is merely to indicate certain synonymity relations between terms we shall use.

We consider a set to be determined by its members, in the sense that "two" sets are identical if they have exactly the same membership lists. This simple dictum has acquired the impressive title *principle of extensionality*.

Our object is to construct an "algebra of sets." Once we have it we shall use it to study sentence structure. A connecting link between sets and sentences is the notion of a predicate, or condition. This link may be described in a rough way as follows. Corresponding to each condition is a collection of things (of an appropriate kind) which satisfy the condition. Thus the set of primes is the collection of those integers which satisfy the condition of primality. The set of isosceles triangles is the collection of all those triangles which satisfy the condition of being isosceles. These matters are discussed in Chapter 3.

In Chapter 3 we shall also examine the structure of some very important types of statements, known as statements with "quantifiers." Such statements abound in mathematics, and therefore require our attention. Many of the subleties of their structure elude satisfactory analysis with the techniques of "traditional" grammar. We shall find, however, that the algebraic techniques made available by our study of sets enable us to treat them in a straightforward manner.

Thus we take the notion of a set as a fundamental concept on which we base our grammatical analysis of sentences. It is a fact, however, that the concept has an importance extending far beyond its applications in grammar: it is one of the most fundamental of all mathematical concepts.

The significance of the set concept rests on the fact that it is an abstraction: instead of bothering with individual "elements," we manage to handle collections of them as if the collections themselves were individuals. We shall accomplish this feat by constructing our algebra in such a way that sets alone are involved: the fact that sets may have "members" or that they may be "collections" of some kind will be ignored in the formal development of the algebra, which we give in Section 3. The algebra developed in Section 3 is based on a list of seven properties, taken there as postulates for that purpose. In Section 1 we state the seven properties, discuss their interpretation as properties of collections of things, consider examples to illustrate some of the notions involved, and have more to say about how we shall proceed. In Section 2 we consider other examples and special cases, we discuss the possibility of alternative interpretations of the seven properties, and we illustrate a claim we shall make that the properties do, in fact, serve to characterize sets. Thus the algebra itself is constructed in Section 3: what is in the first two sections is there to motivate it and to indicate its interpretation and application. In Section 4 we examine the algebra further, analyze its proofs, and compare it to the algebra of statements discussed in the first chapter. Finally, in Chapter 3, we apply it.

Consider, again, the ordinary algebra of numbers. There are operations (addition, multiplication, etc.), relations (equality, inequality), laws (associativity, distributivity, etc.), and derivation rules ("substitution," for example). Given all these, one can proceed with the formal work of algebra. Theoretically, one could even proceed without ever having heard of "numbers" before: without the vaguest idea either of any of the ways numbers might be used (as in counting or measurement, for example) or of what *addition, equality*, etc., might "mean." But one does not. Schools spend years letting children get familiar with numbers, even "used to" them, before starting the serious study of algebra. This is all very wonderful—as, indeed, it ought to be. But it should not obscure the fact that it *is* possible, no matter how unsound it might be considered on pedagogical grounds, to proceed as we indicated above, without the vaguest idea of what algebra is all about: it is possible to treat the whole thing as a kind of simple-minded, formal, or "meaningless," game in which certain marks are to be put on paper according to some definite rules, spelled out in detail.

Not only is all this possible, but the fact that it is possible is extremely important: it provides the key to the significance of mathematical abstraction, and shows why it is so powerful. To say that some mathematical argument can be carried through even if one ignores the "meaning" of what he is doing, or even if he denies the relevance, for the argument, of how it might be interpreted, is not to say that the argument has no meaning or that it cannot be interpreted. Quite the contrary! The point is that it may have several meanings, or many interpretations. We had one example of this sort of thing in Chapter 1, where we constructed an algebra for statements and found that it works just as well as an algebra for certain electrical networks. There are more examples in this chapter and the next two.

1. SOME PROPERTIES OF SETS

In this section we state our postulates for sets and discuss their interpretation. These interpretations are given now to provide some motivation for the formal algebraic work in Section 3. In the next chapter they will be used as the basis for our application of the algebra developed in this chapter.

We discuss two relations (*inclusion* and *equality*) and three operations (*union, intersection*, and *complementation*). Officially, the five terms just mentioned in parentheses will be taken as undefined. Unofficially, however, we "explain" them using the words *set* and *member*. These explanations (or interpretations), set off from the rest of the text by indentation and followed by some examples to illustrate them, provide context for the abstract properties (i) through (vii). It should be noted that there is no reference in any of the abstract properties to *members* or *elements* of sets, or even to the fact that "sets"—whatever they may be—might be capable of having such things as members. Thus, when we extract the properties from context and consider them on their own merits (as we shall do in Section 3), we cannot rely on the interpretation given for them in this section.

However, there is a theorem, due to Marshall Stone, which asserts that the seven properties do indeed characterize sets: that any "system" with all seven of the properties "turns out to be" some collection of quite respectable sets (with members). We shall not prove Stone's theorem, but we shall illustrate it in some simple cases in Sections 2 and 4.

Inclusion

If A and B are sets, we say that A is a *subset* of B, that A is *included* in B, or that B *includes* A, provided each member of A is a member of B. We write $A \subseteq B$ to express this relation. If A is not a subset of B, we write $A \nsubseteq B$.

Thus, for example, the set A of equilateral triangles is a subset of the set B of isosceles triangles, which—in turn—is a subset of the set of all triangles. The set A of all pairs of congruent triangles is a subset of the set B of all pairs of similar triangles. In the first of these examples, A and B are certain collections of triangles. In the second example, A and B are collections each of whose members is itself a collection of triangles: each member of A and each member of B is a collection containing precisely two triangles.

The first of our "abstract" properties asserts simply that any set is a subset of itself:

$$\text{(i)} \quad A \subseteq A,$$

and is expressed by saying that inclusion is a *reflexive* relation. The second abstract property is the assertion that inclusion is *transitive*:

$$\text{(ii)} \quad \text{If } A \subseteq B \text{ and } B \subseteq C, \text{ then } A \subseteq C.$$

Suppose A and B denote sets. If they denote the same set, one writes $A = B$. According to standard usage, $=$ is the sign of synonymity and is placed between expressions which denote the same thing. The principle of extensionality, mentioned in the introductory section, asserts that $A = B$ means that A and B have the same members. In terms of the inclusion relation $\subseteq$, we express this principle as follows:

$$\text{(iii)} \quad A \subseteq B \text{ and } B \subseteq A \text{ if and only if } A = B.$$

Property (iii) provides the connection between the equality relation for sets and the inclusion relation; it says, in part (*only if*), that the inclusion relation is *antisymmetric*.

Before we state the fourth property there are two things we must discuss.
For a variety of compelling reasons we shall confine our attention to
sets which are subsets of some given set. This given set we call our *universe*,
we denote it by U, but we make no assumptions whatever about it or its
members. We use it simply as a source, or supply, of sets—those sets which
are its subsets. Whenever we apply our set algebra, we select some appropriate collection to play the role of U—just which collection we select
depends on the application. Thus, for certain geometrical problems, we
might select as U the set of points in a plane, or in space, or even a collection
of lines or triangles or some other configurations. In an algebraic problem
U might be the set of integers or the set of rational numbers, to give just
two specific examples. This question is discussed further in Chapter 3, where
we shall indicate how confusion, even chaos, may result from carelessness
in specifying U.

For an entirely different set of reasons, we introduce sets without
members, so-called *void* sets or *empty* sets, which we imagine to be subsets
of every set under consideration. It may be reassuring to observe immediately
that there can be no more than one void set. If there were two, each would
be a subset of the other. And hence, by the principle of extensionality, they
must be equal. The unique void set has acquired a name: it is denoted by
the capital letter $\emptyset$ of the Danish alphabet. We shall find that the void set
contributes a great deal to our discussion; among other things, it will allow
us to avoid splitting many of our arguments into a number of tedious special
cases. This will be especially convenient when we discuss intersections, in
this section and later. The void set $\emptyset$ is at least as useful as the number zero,
whose virtues are well known.

The fourth of our abstract properties summarizes the two preceding
paragraphs:

$$\text{(iv)} \quad \emptyset \subseteq A \subseteq U,$$

each set A under consideration is a subset of U and contains the void set
as a subset.

Union

Given any pair A, B of subsets of U, the set whose members are all
members of U which belong to at least one of the given subsets A, B
is called their *union*. We write $A \cup B$ for the union of A and B.

For example, suppose U is the set of living beings, that A is the set of men,
and B is the set of women. Then $A \cup B$ is the set of living people.

All we shall require about unions is the following property: For any
subsets $A, B, C,$ of $U,$

$$\text{(v)} \quad A \subseteq C \text{ and } B \subseteq C \text{ if and only if } A \cup B \subseteq C.$$

Intersection

Given any pair A, B of subsets of U, the set whose members are all members of U which belong to both of the subsets A, B is called their *intersection*. We write $A \cap B$ for the intersection of A and B.

For example, if U is the set of all triangles, A is the set of all right triangles, and B is the set of all isosceles triangles, then $A \cap B$ is the set of all isosceles right triangles (i.e., the set of all "45°" right triangles). It is quite possible that $A \cap B$ be void although neither A nor B is void: suppose, for instance, that A and U are the same as in the previous example, while B is the set of all equilateral triangles.

We summarize what we shall need to know about intersections as follows: For any subsets A, B, C, of U,

(vi) $C \subseteq A$ *and* $C \subseteq B$ *if and only if* $C \subseteq A \cap B$.

There is a kind of "duality" between the union property (v) and the intersection property (vi) which is worth noting: If we interchange $\cup$ and $\cap$, and turn $\subseteq$ around ($\supseteq$), property (v) is converted into property (vi) and vice versa. This observation can be used for the construction of several proofs in later sections.

Complementation

Corresponding to each subset A of U there is another, called its *complement*, whose members are all members of U which are not members of A. We write A' for the complement of A.

For example, in the universe U of all quadrilaterals, the complement of the set A of plane quadrilaterals is the set of skew quadrilaterals. It is extremely important to observe that the "same" set may have different complements in different universes. This may be illustrated by changing U in the previous example to the set of all plane polygons; A' then is the union of the set of all triangles and the set of all plane polygons with five or more sides. Some writers emphasize this point by referring to A' as the *complement of A relative to the universe U.*

Our final abstract property involves complements, intersections, and the inclusion relation: For any subsets A and B of U,

(vii) $A \cap B' = \emptyset$ *if and only if* $A \subseteq B$.

Thus, no subset of B can share any members with the complement of B and—conversely—any subset of U with no members in B' is a subset of B.

In developing the algebra of sets many writers proceed as in the following sample proof for the associativity of intersection.

To show (first) $A \cap (B \cap C) \subseteq (A \cap B) \cap C$. If the left side is void, the result holds; suppose, then, that $A \cap (B \cap C) \neq \emptyset$. Now every member of $A \cap (B \cap C)$ is both a member of A and of $B \cap C$, and hence is a member of each of A, B, C. So every member of $A \cap (B \cap C)$ is a member of both $A \cap B$ and C, and therefore is a member of their intersection. Thus $A \cap (B \cap C) \subseteq (A \cap B) \cap C$. Similarly, $(A \cap B) \cap C \subseteq A \cap (B \cap C)$. Hence

$$A \cap (B \cap C) = (A \cap B) \cap C.$$

The argument may be converted into a proof that union is associative merely by writing $\cup$ for $\cap$, and by changing *intersection* to *union, and* to *or, each* to *one*, and *both* to *either* at crucial points. It is also possible to construct other arguments in the same vein for the commutativity of union and intersection, for distributive laws, etc. We leave the others as exercises.

The proofs that we shall give for all these laws, and others, in Section 3 are quite different. The difference, which is very significant, is not as great as it may seem at first. Some of our proofs are actually quite similar to these: the associativity proofs, for example. But others are very different: distributivity, especially. Our object is to get proofs which do not require us to talk about members of sets. The argument above uses the word *member* half a dozen times in what is really only half of the proof.

We have already mentioned one reason for wanting to avoid discussing members at this stage of the game, but there are others. When we get to Chapter 3, for example, we shall be very interested in properties of individuals which belong to various collections. In particular, we shall devote a good deal of attention to the logical structure of just such statements as appear in the sample proof above. We should be guilty of a horrible logical crime if we "explained" the structure of such statements by appealing to theorems about sets whose proofs were full of statements of the very same kind.

Our program is to show that this circularity can be avoided—that we can work out our set algebra without talking about members, that we can justify the proofs needed for this project using the theory of inference we already have, and finally that with set algebra as the basis we can proceed to the study of sentence structure and of more elaborate forms of inference. Among some of these "more elaborate" forms of inference are those used in the "sample proof" above.

Properties (i) through (vii) are the fundamental properties of sets which we take as starting point for our algebra of sets. Because there are plenty of other properties which might be chosen for that honor instead of, or in addition to, these, it is appropriate to say a few words in defense of this particular list.

Suppose we had two lists of properties and that from each of them we could deduce all the theorems we want to get. From the point of view of having all the "right" consequences, one list would be just as good as the other. One way to choose between two such lists might be based on a comparison of their lengths.

An extreme case ("dogmatism") is that in which a list contains all the theorems: one advantage (?) enjoyed in this case is that there is nothing to prove, but there is an awful lot one has to swallow. As a less extreme version of such dogmatism one may include a few of the "theorems" among the postulates, for example those whose proofs are the hardest. This option is quite sound from a mathematical point of view, and is certainly available to any reader willing to accept the responsibility for electing it. It should be mentioned, however, that one does not get something for nothing: either he must work through a proof step by step, or he must be prepared to accept the entire result in one gulp. Thus the choice left to the reader is between skepticism and credulity.

Our list is short enough to make the proofs interesting and long enough to get the results we want. It is also important in "higher" mathematics: properties (i) through (iii) define a *partially ordered* set and (i) through (vi) a *lattice* (with identities). The whole list characterizes a *Boolean algebra*; indeed the work in Sections 3 and 4 amounts to a proof of this last assertion.

2. A SPECIAL CASE: FINITE SETS

Before settling down, in Section 3, to the serious business of turning out a string of consequences of the seven properties, we examine a very special and quite simple kind of set, introduce a piece of notation we shall have occasion to use frequently, draw some pictures, and look at an easy case of Stone's theorem.

Sets with no, one, two, or three members are examples of "finite" sets. Indeed, the void set and any set whose members can be "counted" using ordinary whole numbers (= positive integers) are finite. The set of all people in the world is finite, and, according to one cosmological theory, the set of all electrons and protons in the physical universe is finite. The set of all positive integers, however, is not finite. Sets which are not finite are said to be "infinite." It is possible to formulate rigorous general criteria for the finiteness of arbitrary sets. These criteria are rather subtle and will not be considered here. Our attention will be devoted entirely to specific examples of sets, whose classification we shall presume to be beyond dispute.

Brackets and Membership Lists

If A is a set with just three members a, b, c, it is the custom to write $A = \{a, b, c\}$. More generally, we obtain a descriptive name for any nonvoid finite set by enclosing a list of its members in brackets. Thus

$$\{2, 3, 5, 7, 11, 13, 17, 19\}$$

is a name for the set of the eight primes which are less than 20. In view of the principle of extensionality, the order in which members are listed is quite irrelevant; indeed,

$$\{2, 5, 11, 17, 19, 7, 13, 3\} = \{2, 3, 5, 7, 11, 13, 17, 19\}.$$

Intrepid writers adapt the bracket notation to the case of sets having lengthy membership lists by introducing an ellipsis. Thus $\{1, 2, 3, \ldots, 99\}$ might denote the set of all positive integers less than 100. The danger of ambiguity inherent in this practice arises from the fact that very few of the members (here, less than 5%) are actually mentioned, while the remaining members are left to the reader's imagination. Prudence dictates that such "partially descriptive" names for sets be used only when supplemented by enough explanation to dispel confusion. Subject to the same restriction, brackets are even used in the case of some infinite sets. One often finds the set of all positive integers denoted by

$$\{1, 2, 3, \ldots\}.$$

In the case of infinite sets, explanatory remarks are obligatory; the ellipsis cannot be eliminated, even in principle.

We have seen, as a consequence of the principle of extensionality, that the order in which the members of a set are listed is quite immaterial. Another consequence of the same principle is that duplication in such lists is always avoidable. Thus the sets

$$\{1, 2, 3\}, \qquad \{1, 2, 3, 2, 3\}$$

are equal, because each member of either is a member of the other.

A set with just one member is a tricky thing and must be handled with care. Such sets are often called *singletons*. The distinction between a singleton and its member is sharp, although—as distinctions go—it is a rather fine one. For example, $\{\emptyset\}$ is a set with one member, namely $\emptyset$; but $\emptyset$ is a set with no members. In view of the principle of extensionality, $\emptyset \neq \{\emptyset\}$. More generally, although $a \in \{a\}$, we are never entitled to write $a = \{a\}$. In particular, if A is itself a set, we have

$$A \in \{A\}, \quad \text{but} \quad A \nsubseteq \{A\} \quad \text{unless} \quad A = \emptyset.$$

If A is neither void nor is itself a singleton, it is a "larger" set than $\{A\}$ in the sense that it has more members; $\{A\}$ is a set with just one member.

This distinction has an analogy in law. The courts have decided that firing a government employee may be a breach of contract, although Congress has the right to abolish the office he holds (e.g., by cutting it out of the budget). Thus Congress can do some things to collections of individuals, even singletons, which it has no right to do to individuals themselves.

On the other hand, it *is* possible, in a suitably complicated universe, for one set to be both a member and a subset of another set. One example of such a pair is given by $\emptyset$ and $\{\emptyset\}$: here $\emptyset \in \{\emptyset\}$ and also $\emptyset \subseteq \{\emptyset\}$. More generally, suppose that $B = A \cup \{A\}$. Thus B is the union of A and the singleton $\{A\}$. Since

$$A \subseteq A \cup \{A\} \qquad \text{and} \qquad \{A\} \subseteq A \cup \{A\},$$

we have both

$$A \subseteq B \qquad \text{and} \qquad \{A\} \subseteq B.$$

Because $\{A\} \subseteq B$, each member of $\{A\}$ is a member of B; but A is the only member of $\{A\}$. So $A \in B$, as well as $A \subseteq B$. In this situation, B has one member—namely A—which is not a member of A; if A is a finite set, then the number of members of B is just one more than the number of members of A. (In this course we refrain from discussing the "number" of members of any sets but finite sets. Readers interested in such matters may consult books on set theory. Any who do will find that the word *finite* cannot be omitted from the sentence preceding these parenthetical remarks.)

This particular construction is interesting because it was used, by von Neumann, as a technique for building "numbers" with the "material" made available by the theory of sets. Observe, indeed, that the sets in the following list,

$$\emptyset, \quad \emptyset \cup \{\emptyset\}, \quad \emptyset \cup \{\emptyset\} \cup \{\emptyset \cup \{\emptyset\}\},$$
$$\emptyset \cup \{\emptyset\} \cup \{\emptyset \cup \{\emptyset\}\} \cup \{\emptyset \cup \{\emptyset\} \cup \{\emptyset \cup \{\emptyset\}\}\}, \ldots$$

have, respectively, no, one, two, three, ... members. The list is constructed as follows: $\emptyset$ is first, and for each set A of the list the next set is $A \cup \{A\}$. The sets listed above can be written more compactly as follows:

$$\emptyset, \quad \{\emptyset\}, \quad \{\emptyset, \{\emptyset\}\}, \quad \{\emptyset, \{\emptyset\}, \{\emptyset, \{\emptyset\}\}\}, \ldots$$

because $\emptyset \cup A = A$, for any set A, and $\{a\} \cup \{b\} = \{a, b\}$. Von Neumann introduced "names" for these sets: let 0 be $\emptyset$, 1 be $\{\emptyset\}$, 2 be $\{\emptyset, \{\emptyset\}\}$, 3 be $\{\emptyset, \{\emptyset\}, \{\emptyset, \{\emptyset\}\}\}$, etc. Then

$$1 = \{0\}, \ 2 = \{0, 1\}, \ 3 = \{0, 1, 2\}, \text{ etc.,}$$

and the list is just

$$0, 1, 2, 3, \ldots.$$

To claim that numbers are sets may seem rather like saying there is no Santa Claus, but a little reflection must convince anyone that such a claim should not be taken seriously. The problem—which is considered further in the Appendix—is not what numbers might be, but, whatever they are, whether the concepts and techniques of "set theory" are sophisticated enough to permit us to produce numbers, or at least reasonable facsimiles thereof. Why anybody should ever think of trying to do so is another question entirely, which we leave for the Appendix.

Hasse Diagrams

A singleton has only two subsets: itself and
the void set. We may depict these subsets
in what is called a *Hasse diagram*:

Consider next a set with two members, say $\{a, b\}$. This set has four subsets,
illustrated in the following diagram:

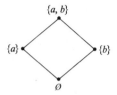

For a set with three members, there are eight subsets:

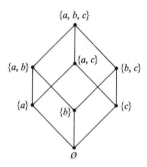

In these diagrams, two subsets are connected by a rising path if and only if
the lower one is a subset of the higher one. Similar diagrams may be constructed for larger finite sets, although they rapidly become quite elaborate:
a set with n members has 2^n subsets ($2^4 = 16$, $2^5 = 32$, $2^6 = 64$, ...,
$2^{10} = 1024$, etc.). As an example, the diagram for $n = 4$ may be drawn
as shown in the accompanying figure.

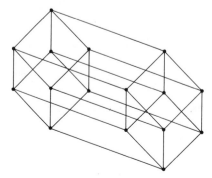

We leave the others as exercises for the interested reader.

Family trees and organizational charts provide other opportunities for drawing Hasse diagrams. Indeed, any hierarchy is based on a transitive relation and may be so depicted. For sets the relation is *inclusion*, for a family tree it is *descendent*, etc.

Various formal properties of the relation are reflected in its Hasse diagram by the presence or absence of certain configurations. For example, although properties (i) through (iii) are "automatic," property (iv) requires that the diagram come to a point at both top and bottom. A chart of military command comes to a point at the top (representing the commander-in-chief), but not at the bottom (if there is more than one private soldier).

If a couple (a, b) has two children (c, d), the Hasse diagram for their family tree contains the following configuration,

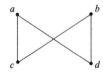

which cannot appear in a Hasse diagram for the subsets of any set. It is ruled out both by (v) and by (vi).

Indeed, (v) implies that, whatever $c \cup d$ may be, it has to be above both c and d and below everything else above them. No point in the diagram has this property. Similarly (vi) implies that, whatever $a \cap b$ is, it is below both a and b and above everything else below them.

Thus both (v) and (vi) require at least one thing below both of a, b and above both of c, d:

(The lines joining a to c and b to d are omitted as superfluous.) Here e and f may or may not be the same: at any rate, people do not happen to reproduce this way.

We may even use Hasse diagrams to define abstract systems with some or all of the properties (i) through (vii). The three systems diagrammed at the top of p. 59, for example, each have all of the properties (i) through (vi). In Section 3 we shall find that

$$A \cup A' = U \quad \text{and} \quad A \cap A' = \emptyset$$

are among the consequences of properties (i) through (vii). Thus in any system having all seven properties, each member may be paired with another in such a way that for each pair, the "union" goes all the way up to the "top" and the "intersection" goes all the way down to the "bottom." In the first of the three systems above it is not possible to pair off the elements so that this happens. In the other two systems such pairings are possible, but property (vii) does not hold for any of them. (Cf. Exercise 4 below.)

Stone's Theorem

Suppose that we have some system ℬ with operations ∪, ∩ and complement, and relations =, ⊆ satisfying all of the properties (i) through (vii). Stone proved that there is a set S and a collection ℭ of subsets of S with the following properties:

> The members $a, b, \ldots$ of the given system ℬ and the subsets $A, B, \ldots$ in ℭ can be paired one-to-one in such a way that if a is paired with A and b with B, then $a \cup b$ is paired with $A \cup B$, $a \cap b$ with $A \cap B$, and a' with A', while $a \subseteq b$ if and only if $A \subseteq B$.

Two systems, related as are ℬ and ℭ here, are simply duplicates of each other. Although the elements in the two systems may be described or classified differently, they are paired to each other in such a way that every relation or operation in either system has an exact counterpart in the other. In Stone's proof, he shows how the set S may be constructed from ℬ: the members of S may, in fact, be taken to be certain subsets of ℬ or (in some of the simpler cases) they may be certain elements of ℬ.

We can illustrate Stone's theorem in a very special case in the following way: We present an apparently distorted interpretation of properties (i) through (vii) and then observe that this interpretation may be reinterpreted as, or represented by, a collection of subsets of an appropriate set. Thus our new interpretation, which is arithmetical, and may itself be described without direct reference to sets, will turn out to be "essentially" a collection of sets "in disguise."

We consider the integer 30 and its positive integral factors 1, 2, 3, 5, 6, 10, 15, 30. Let us interpret $a \subseteq b$, where a, b denote factors of 30, as meaning that a is a factor of b. For example: $1 \subseteq 2, 2 \subseteq 2, 2 \subseteq 6, 5 \subseteq 15$, but $3 \nsubseteq 10$, etc. Of the factors of 30, there is only one, 1, which is a factor of all: let it play the role of ∅. Let 30 itself play the role of U. With these interpretations, properties (i) through (iv) are all satisfied:

(i′) $a \subseteq a$.

(ii′) If $a \subseteq b$ and $b \subseteq c$, then $a \subseteq c$.

(iii′) $a \subseteq b$ and $b \subseteq a$ if and only if $a = b$.

(iv′) $1 \subseteq a \subseteq 30$.

Write $a \cup b$ for the "least common multiple" of a, b. Thus

$$1 \cup 2 = 2, \quad 2 \cup 3 = 6, \quad 6 \cup 15 = 30, \quad 5 \cup 30 = 30, \quad \text{etc.}$$

Then

(v′) $a \subseteq c$ and $b \subseteq c$ if and only if $a \cup b \subseteq c$.

Write $a \cap b$ for the "greatest common factor" of a, b. Thus

$$1 \cap 2 = 1, \quad 2 \cap 3 = 1, \quad 6 \cap 15 = 3, \quad 5 \cap 30 = 5, \quad \text{etc.}$$

Then

(vi′) $c \subseteq a$ and $c \subseteq b$ if and only if $c \subseteq a \cap b$.

Finally write a' for the quotient of 30 by a. Thus

$$2' = 15, \quad 3' = 10, \quad 15' = 2, \quad \text{etc.}$$

Note that $(a')' = a$, so that a is the complement of a'. Then

(vii′) $a \cap b' = 1$ if and only if $a \subseteq b$.

In this interpretation, (vii′) depends on the fact that no factor of 30 shares with its "complement" any factor greater than 1. This follows from the observation that 30, which is $2 \cdot 3 \cdot 5$, is not divisible by the square of any prime; so no pair of complementary factors can share any common prime factors. Here (vii′) states that a and b' have no common factor greater than 1 if and only if all factors of a are factors of b, the complement of b'.

A Hasse diagram reveals the secret:

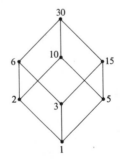

Here a and b are joined by rising lines if a is a factor of b. Our "sets" are not hard to find: each of the numbers we consider may be represented by the set of its prime factors. Using them we relabel the diagram, taking into account the fact that 1 has no prime factors; and it is immediately apparent that we have reproduced the diagram we used earlier to depict the family of subsets of a set with three members:

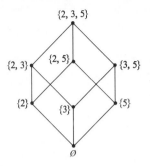

We hasten to emphasize that we have not proved Stone's theorem—we have not even stated it completely. The full theorem is quite deep and well beyond the scope of this course. We may claim only to have illustrated it in a very simple special case.

Our study of this simple example illustrates two extremely important ideas:

1. The first has to do with the latitude of interpretation permitted when one confronts a postulate system. A system of postulates is required to embody everything one is supposed to know, or have at his disposal, for the development of a theory. Hence the conclusion that complete latitude of interpretation must be allowed: the only criterion for acceptability of an interpretation is that it fits all the postulates. In our example, we verified that our arithmetical interpretation of the set postulates does fit. If one were required to restrict his latitude of interpretation for some reason or other, he has grounds for a claim that the system of postulates is inadequate—that it does not, in fact, embody everything one is supposed to know initially for the theory under consideration. It is a corollary of these observations that a discussion of "meaning" in connection with postulate systems is a very delicate matter. Any postulate system is certainly constructed with a very definite "meaning" in mind: it is constructed in accord with its intended interpretation—or interpretations, if there is to be more than one. But what such interpretations may be is quite irrelevant as far as the business of drawing consequences from the postulates is concerned: whatever follows from the postulates must hold in any interpretation that fits the postulates.

The concern about interpretation of postulate systems and the inclination to discount whatever "meaning" they may have are attitudes characteristic of twentieth-century mathematics. Until some sixty or seventy years ago, the greater effort seems to have been expended on the construction of postulate systems capable of being interpreted in only one way. Examples are the postulate systems for geometry, due to Euclid, Legendre, Hilbert, and others, and the postulate systems for numbers, due to Peano and others. More recently, however, the trend has been to emphasize the importance of so-called *noncategorical* postulate systems: systems permitting more than one interpretation; indeed, the more the better. In this game one must take pains to avoid letting any specific interpretation interfere with the generality of deductions. It is precisely here that the great power of mathematical abstraction is revealed. We shall encounter an example in the next section.

2. The other important idea illustrated by our example is that, given two mathematical "systems," one of them may turn out to be the other "in disguise." A more sophisticated way of expressing this fact is to say that the systems are *abstractly identical*, or *isomorphic*. (*Iso* is Greek for *same*, *morphos* means *shape* or *form*.) This notion is one of the key ideas in modern abstract mathematics.

EXERCISES

1. Suppose A is a set with four members a, b, c, d: $A = \{a, b, c, d\}$. Assign each of the sixteen subsets of A to one of the dots in the Hasse diagram which the text alleges is capable of representing the inclusion relations holding between them. *Note.* There is more than one way to make these assignments. Determine the number of different ways they may be made.

2. Draw a Hasse diagram for the positive integral factors of 210 and show how this system may be represented as a collection of subsets of an appropriate set.

3. (a) Draw a Hasse diagram for the positive integral factors of 12.
   (b) Some, but not all, of the seven properties hold for the system mentioned in part (a). Determine which hold and which do not.

4. Prove that none of the three five-element systems defined in the text using Hasse diagrams has all seven of the properties (i), . . . , (vii). Besides the three in the text, there are two other five-element systems which have properties (i) through (vi):

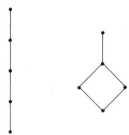

   Prove that neither of these two has property (vii).

5. There are sixteen different six-element systems with properties (i) through (iv). Draw Hasse diagrams for as many as you can find, and determine which of them have property (vii).

6. For systems such as those in Exercises 3, 4, 5 (which are examples of so-called *lattices*), the following distributive laws may or may not hold:

$$w \cap (x \cup y) = (w \cap x) \cup (w \cap y),$$
$$w \cup (x \cap y) = (w \cup x) \cap (w \cup y).$$

Actually both hold for the system in Exercise 3 and for three of the five-element systems in Exercise 4, but both fail for the systems

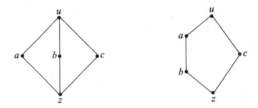

Find counterexamples to show that neither of these lattices is "distributive."

7. The finite systems satisfying (i) through (vii) which we have examined, in the text and in Exercise 2 above, can be represented by the collection of *all* subsets of some set. This situation is typical only for finite systems. For an arbitrary infinite system, the best one can expect is to obtain a representation by means of *some* of the subsets of a set. For an example, consider subsets of the set of positive integers. Let us say that a set of positive integers is a *Stone* set if it is finite, or if its complement is finite. It follows from this definition that A', $A \cap B$, and $A \cup B$ are Stone sets if A and B are; and, indeed, that the collection of all Stone sets has properties (i) through (vii).

Show, however, that there are some sets of positive integers which are not Stone sets. (It is sufficient to describe a set of positive integers which is not finite and whose complement is not finite.) It is proved in books on set theory that only finite sets have "denumerably" many subsets. From this result it follows that the collection of Stone sets (which is denumerable but not finite) cannot be represented by the family of all subsets of any set.

3. ALGEBRA OF SUBSETS OF A UNIVERSE

The business of this section is the derivation of a number of consequences of properties (i) through (vii), the postulates for our algebra of sets. Some features of this project deserve special mention.

First, we have the consequences themselves. Just what they are can be determined by glancing at the statements of the theorems in this section, and at the exercises. Even a cursory survey will reveal that the results obtained bear, at the very least, a striking resemblance to the laws of our algebra of statements. We shall have a good deal to say about the connection between these two algebras at the end of this section, and in the next section.

Next, there are the "algebraic" techniques used in proving the theorems of this section. To see what they are one cannot be content just to look at the theorems themselves, he must look at the proofs of at least some of the theorems. A fair bit of the work in Chapter 3 presupposes some knowledge of these techniques. How many of the proofs deserve careful study is a decision we leave for the reader; the exercises afford opportunities to check comprehension and develop skill.

Finally, there is a more sophisticated question: what is it about these so-called proofs that entitles them to be accepted as proofs? This, of course, is part of a much larger—and very important—complex of questions, to which we are obliged to devote attention: just what are mathematical proofs, how are they put together, and how can they be identified? In Section 4 we analyze the logical structure of the proofs given in this section. We shall find that it is possible to carry out this analysis entirely in terms of the simple theory of inference developed in Chapter 1.

All the proofs in this section are based on properties (i) through (vii), collected here in "symbolic" form:

(i) $P \subseteq P$.

(ii) If $P \subseteq Q$ and $Q \subseteq R$, then $P \subseteq R$.

(iii) $P \subseteq Q$ and $Q \subseteq P$ if and only if $P = Q$.

(iv) $\emptyset \subseteq P \subseteq U$.

(v) $P \subseteq R$ and $Q \subseteq R$ if and only if $P \cup Q \subseteq R$.

(vi) $R \subseteq P$ and $R \subseteq Q$ if and only if $R \subseteq P \cap Q$.

(vii) $P \cap Q' = \emptyset$ if and only if $P \subseteq Q$.

Our work in this section is symbolic, just as our treatment of algebraic derivation in the statement algebra was symbolic: if the free symbols P, Q, R in properties (i) through (vii) and their consequences are replaced by names for subsets of U, we obtain specific assertions about subsets of U. As we did in the statement algebra, we shall employ the "specialization" maneuver without comment. Analogues of the other rules used in Chapter 1 will be found in Theorem 1, Theorems 2(3) and 4(3), and in the corollary to Theorem 6.

The first theorem lists some of the familiar properties of the equality relation.

Theorem 1 Equality is reflexive, symmetric, and transitive:

(1) $P = P$.

(2) If $P = Q$, then $Q = P$.

(3) If $P = Q$ and $Q = R$, then $P = R$.

Proof. By (i), $P \subseteq P$; hence with P for Q in (iii), it follows that $P = P$. This proves (1). Next, if $P = Q$, then by the "if" part of (iii), $P \subseteq Q$ and $Q \subseteq P$. But, by the "only if" part, if $Q \subseteq P$ and $P \subseteq Q$, then $Q = P$, and we have proved (2). Finally, if $P = Q$ and $Q = R$, then [(iii)]

$$P \subseteq Q \quad \text{and} \quad Q \subseteq P$$

and

$$Q \subseteq R \quad \text{and} \quad R \subseteq Q;$$

that is,

$$P \subseteq Q \quad \text{and} \quad Q \subseteq R$$

and

$$R \subseteq Q \quad \text{and} \quad Q \subseteq P;$$

so [(ii)]

$$P \subseteq R \quad \text{and} \quad R \subseteq P,$$

and hence [(iii)]

$$P = R. \quad \text{Q.E.D.}$$

The next two theorems list several properties of the union operation.

Theorem 2

(1) $P \subseteq P \cup Q$ and $Q \subseteq P \cup Q$.

(2) If $P \subseteq Q$, then $P \cup R \subseteq Q \cup R$.

(3) If $P = Q$, then $P \cup R = Q \cup R$.

Proof. By (i), $P \cup Q \subseteq P \cup Q$; hence, taking $P \cup Q$ for R in (v),

$$P \subseteq P \cup Q \quad \text{and} \quad Q \subseteq P \cup Q.$$

For (2) note that if $P \subseteq Q$, then $P \subseteq Q \cup R$, by (ii), since $Q \subseteq Q \cup R$ by (1). Also $R \subseteq Q \cup R$. Now using (v) with R for Q and $Q \cup R$ for R, from $P \subseteq Q \cup R$ and $R \subseteq Q \cup R$, we get

$$P \cup R \subseteq Q \cup R.$$

For (3) we use (2), which we have just proved, and (iii): if $P = Q$, then $P \subseteq Q$ and $Q \subseteq P$, so

$$P \cup R \subseteq Q \cup R \quad \text{and} \quad Q \cup R \subseteq P \cup R;$$

hence

$$P \cup R = Q \cup R.$$

In the following theorem we begin to see formal analogies with the statement algebra of Chapter 1. This theorem lists properties of union analogous to those basic laws for disjunction bearing the same names. Here $\emptyset$ and U are the analogues of O and I. Theorem 5, below, establishes the corresponding relation between set intersection and statement conjunction.

Theorem 3

(1) $P \cup P = P$ (Idempotence)

(2) $P \cup U = U$ (Identity)

(3) $\varnothing \cup P = P$ (Identity)

(4) $P \cup Q = Q \cup P$ (Commutative)

(5) $P \cup (Q \cup R) = (P \cup Q) \cup R$ (Associative)

Proof

(1) $P \subseteq P \cup P$, by Theorem 2(1) with P for Q. By (i), $P \subseteq P$; hence, by (v), $P \cup P \subseteq P$. Therefore, by (iii), $P \cup P = P$.

(2) By (i), $U \subseteq U$, and by (iv), $P \subseteq U$; hence [(v)] $P \cup U \subseteq U$. But [Theorem 2(1)] $U \subseteq P \cup U$, so [(iii)] $P \cup U = U$.

(3) By (iv) $\varnothing \subseteq P$ and by (i) $P \subseteq P$, so [(v)] $\varnothing \cup P \subseteq P$. By Theorem 2(1), $P \subseteq \varnothing \cup P$. Hence $\varnothing \cup P = P$.

(4) By Theorem 2(1), $P \subseteq Q \cup P$ and $Q \subseteq Q \cup P$, so by (v)

$$P \cup Q \subseteq Q \cup P.$$

Similarly $Q \cup P \subseteq P \cup Q$; hence

$$P \cup Q = Q \cup P.$$

(5) $Q \subseteq P \cup Q$ and $P \cup Q \subseteq (P \cup Q) \cup R$, so

$$Q \subseteq (P \cup Q) \cup R.$$

But $R \subseteq (P \cup Q) \cup R$, so

$$Q \cup R \subseteq (P \cup Q) \cup R.$$

Also $P \subseteq (P \cup Q) \cup R$; hence

$$P \cup (Q \cup R) \subseteq (P \cup Q) \cup R.$$

Similarly

$$(P \cup Q) \cup R \subseteq P \cup (Q \cup R).$$

Hence (5).

Theorems 4 and 5 are exact counterparts, for intersection, of Theorems 2 and 3. Their proofs are left as exercises.

Theorem 4

(1) $P \cap Q \subseteq P$ and $P \cap Q \subseteq Q$.

(2) If $P \subseteq Q$, then $P \cap R \subseteq Q \cap R$.

(3) If $P = Q$, then $P \cap R = Q \cap R$.

Theorem 5

(1) $P \cap P = P$	(Idempotence)
(2) $P \cap U = P$	(Identity)
(3) $\emptyset \cap P = \emptyset$	(Identity)
(4) $P \cap Q = Q \cap P$	(Commutative)
(5) $P \cap (Q \cap R) = (P \cap Q) \cap R$	(Associative)

EXERCISES

1. Fill in the details (including justifications) of the proof outlined above for part (5) of Theorem 3.
2. Prove Theorems 4 and 5. This may be done by adapting proofs of Theorems 2 and 3, the difference being the use of property (vi) where appropriate instead of property (v).

Prove the following consequences of properties (i) through (vi):

3. $P \cap (P \cup Q) = P$　(Absorption)
4. $P \cup (P \cap Q) = P$　(Absorption)
5. $P \cup (Q \cap R) \subseteq (P \cup Q) \cap (P \cup R)$
6. $(P \cap Q) \cup (P \cap R) \subseteq P \cap (Q \cup R)$
7. $(P \cap Q) \cup (P \cap R) \cup (Q \cap R) \subseteq (P \cup Q) \cap (P \cup R) \cap (Q \cup R)$
8. If $P \subseteq R$ and $Q \subseteq S$, then

$$P \cup Q \subseteq R \cup S \quad \text{and} \quad P \cap Q \subseteq R \cap S.$$

9. $P \subseteq Q$ if and only if $P \cup Q = Q$.
10. $P \subseteq Q$ if and only if $P \cap Q = P$.
11. $(P \cap Q) \cup R \subseteq P \cap (Q \cup R)$ if and only if $R \subseteq P$.
12. $P \cap (Q \cup R) \subseteq (P \cap Q) \cup (P \cap R)$ if and only if

$$(P \cup Q) \cap (P \cup R) \subseteq P \cup (Q \cap R).$$

Hint: For the *if* part,

$P \cap (Q \cup R) = [P \cap (P \cup R)] \cap (Q \cup R)$	[Abs: Ex. 3
$= P \cap [(P \cup R) \cap (Q \cup R)]$	[Assoc
$= P \cap [(R \cup P) \cap (R \cup Q)]$	[Comm
$\subseteq P \cap [R \cup (P \cap Q)]$	[Hyp $(R, P, Q$ for P, Q, R, resp.)
$= [(P \cap Q) \cup P] \cap [(P \cap Q) \cup R]$	[Abs: Ex. 4, Comm
$\subseteq (P \cap Q) \cup (P \cap R)$	[Hyp $(P \cap Q, P$ for P, Q, resp.)

So far we have seen that using only properties (i) through (vi), we can derive analogues for all the basic laws of Chapter 1 except for the distributive laws and those involving the negation sign (complement, involution and De Morgan). We saw (Exercise 6, page 63) that the distributive laws cannot be deduced from properties (i) through (vi) alone. We have also seen (Exercises 5 and 6, above) that "half" of each law does follow from (i) through (vi) and (Exercise 12, above) that it will suffice to get only the other "half" of either one.

Our next job is to take (vii) into account, along with (i) through (vi), and to derive the analogues of the complement, involution and De Morgan laws. Finally, we shall obtain the missing part of the distributive law (Theorem 8).

We begin with a pair of lemmas. The first provides analogues for some of the complement laws (the others are left as exercises); the second states the involution law.

Lemma 1 $P \cap P' = \emptyset$ and $U' = \emptyset$.

Proof. Because set inclusion is reflexive, $P \cap P' = \emptyset$ follows from (vii), with P for Q. Putting U for P in what we just proved, we have $U \cap U' = \emptyset$. But with U' for P in Theorem 5(2), we get $U' = U \cap U'$, which takes care of this lemma.

Lemma 2 $P = (P')'$.

Proof. By Lemma 1, with P' for P, $P' \cap (P')' = \emptyset$ and, since intersection is commutative, $(P')' \cap P' = \emptyset$. Then, by (vii), we have $(P')' \subseteq P$, which is half of what we want to prove. Replacing P by P' in $(P')' \subseteq P$ gives $((P')')' \subseteq P'$, which [by Theorem 4(2)] gives

$$P \cap ((P')')' \subseteq P \cap P'.$$

So, by Lemma 1 again, $P \cap ((P')')' = \emptyset$; and $P \subseteq (P')'$ by (vii) again. Q.E.D.

Theorem 6 $P \subseteq Q$ if and only if $Q' \subseteq P'$.

Proof. It will suffice to prove $Q' \subseteq P'$ if $P \subseteq Q$, for the latter implies its own converse: putting Q' and P', respectively, for P and Q gives

$$(P')' \subseteq (Q')' \quad \text{if} \quad Q' \subseteq P';$$

so, by Lemma 2,

$$P \subseteq Q \quad \text{if} \quad Q' \subseteq P'.$$

Now, if $P \subseteq Q$, then $P \cap Q' \subseteq Q \cap Q'$, by Theorem 4(2); and, by Lemma 1, it follows that $P \cap Q' = \emptyset$, or $Q' \cap P = \emptyset$. Hence, by Lemma 2, $Q' \cap (P')' = \emptyset$ and finally, by (vii), $Q' \subseteq P'$.

Corollary $P = Q$ if and only if $P' = Q'$.

Theorem 7 (De Morgan)

(1) $(P \cap Q)' = P' \cup Q'$.

(2) $(P \cup Q)' = P' \cap Q'$.

Proof. By Theorem 4(1),

$$P \cap Q \subseteq P \quad \text{and} \quad P \cap Q \subseteq Q.$$

So, by Theorem 6,

$$P' \subseteq (P \cap Q)' \quad \text{and} \quad Q' \subseteq (P \cap Q)'$$

and, by (v),

$$P' \cup Q' \subseteq (P \cap Q)',$$

which is half of Theorem 7(1). The other half is analogous: by Theorem 2(1),

$$P' \subseteq P' \cup Q' \quad \text{and} \quad Q' \subseteq P' \cup Q';$$

by Theorem 6 and Lemma 2,

$$(P' \cup Q')' \subseteq P \quad \text{and} \quad (P' \cup Q')' \subseteq Q;$$

so, by (vi),

$$(P' \cup Q')' \subseteq P \cap Q;$$

and, Theorem 6 again,

$$(P \cap Q)' \subseteq P' \cup Q'.$$

Part (2) follows from part (1): first, by the corollary,

$$P \cap Q = (P' \cup Q')',$$

and, with P' for P and Q' for Q,

$$P' \cap Q' = (P \cup Q)'. \quad \text{Q.E.D.}$$

EXERCISES

1. Prove the corollary to Theorem 6. [Use (iii).]
2. $\varnothing' = U$. [Use Lemmas 1, 2 and the corollary.]
3. $P \cup P' = U$. [Lemma 1 and Theorem 7.]
4. $P \subseteq Q$ if and only if $P' \cup Q = U$. [Theorem 7, Property (vii).]
5. $Q = P'$ if and only if $P \cap Q = \varnothing$ and $P \cup Q = U$.
6. $P \subseteq Q$ if and only if $P \subseteq P' \cup Q$. [Apply Exercise 9, page 67, to $P \subseteq P' \cup Q$, and use Exercise 4 above.]

With one more lemma we can get the distributive laws.

Lemma 3 $P \cap (P' \cup Q) \subseteq Q$.

Proof. If $R = P \cap (P' \cup Q)$, then $R \subseteq P$ and $P' \subseteq R'$. Hence

$$P' \cup Q \subseteq R' \cup Q.$$

But $R \subseteq P' \cup Q$, so $R \subseteq R' \cup Q$. Then, by Exercise 6 above, $R \subseteq Q$.

Theorem 8 (*Distributivity*)

$$P \cup (Q \cap R) = (P \cup Q) \cap (P \cup R),$$
$$P \cap (Q \cup R) = (P \cap Q) \cup (P \cap R).$$

Proof. In view of Exercises 5, 6, and 12, page 67, it is sufficient to prove, say,

$$(P \cup Q) \cap (P \cup R) \subseteq P \cup (Q \cap R).$$

Let

$$S = (P \cup Q) \cap (P \cup R), \qquad T = P \cup (Q \cap R),$$
$$V = S \cap T'.$$

We are to prove $S \subseteq T$, which, by property (vii), amounts to $V = \emptyset$. First $V \subseteq S$, so $V \subseteq P \cup Q$ and $V \subseteq P \cup R$. But $V \subseteq T'$ and $T' = P' \cap (Q \cap R)'$, so $V \subseteq P'$ and $V \subseteq (Q \cap R)'$. Hence

$$V \subseteq P' \cap (P \cup Q)$$

and, by Lemma 3, $V \subseteq Q$. Similarly,

$$V \subseteq P' \cap (P \cup R) \subseteq R.$$

Hence

$$V \subseteq Q \cap R \qquad \text{and} \qquad V \subseteq (Q \cap R) \cap (Q \cap R)' = \emptyset. \quad \text{Q.E.D.}$$

In this section we have derived a number of consequences of properties (i) through (vii). Among these consequences we find "analogues" for all the so-called "basic properties" of our algebra of statements. It follows that each consequence of the basic laws of our statement algebra has an analogue in our set algebra. It is equally noteworthy that there are proofs, in the respective algebras, of such analogues which are themselves perfectly analogous, step by step. From a "formal" point of view, the differences between these algebras consist only of a few variations in the notation. In the statement algebra we use lower-case symbols $(p, q, r, \ldots)$, three lines $(\equiv)$ for the equivalence relation, "angular" operation signs $(\wedge, \vee)$, a tilde for negation, and O, I for the "identities"; their correspondents in the set algebra are respectively upper case symbols $(P, Q, R, \ldots)$, two lines $(=)$ for the equality relation, "rounded" operation signs $(\cap, \cup)$, an accent for complement, and $\emptyset, U$ for the "identities." We emphasize this similarity between the two algebras by writing out as examples a pair of analogous proofs of analogous results. Excepting the differences of notation just mentioned, these proofs are identical, even to the authorities cited for the several steps in the argument.

Example 1

$$\sim[(p \wedge q) \vee (\bar{p} \wedge \bar{q})] \equiv (\bar{q} \wedge p) \vee (\bar{p} \wedge q).$$

Proof

$\sim[(p \wedge q) \vee (\bar{p} \wedge \bar{q})]$

$\equiv \sim(p \wedge q) \wedge [\sim(\bar{p} \wedge \bar{q})]$	[De M
$\equiv (\bar{p} \vee \bar{q}) \wedge (p \vee q)$	[De M, Inv
$\equiv [(\bar{p} \vee \bar{q}) \wedge p] \vee [(\bar{p} \vee \bar{q}) \wedge q]$	[Distr
$\equiv (\bar{p} \wedge p) \vee (\bar{q} \wedge p) \vee (\bar{p} \wedge q) \vee (\bar{q} \wedge q)$	[Distr
$\equiv O \vee (\bar{q} \wedge p) \vee (\bar{p} \wedge q) \vee O$	[Comp
$\equiv (\bar{q} \wedge p) \vee (\bar{p} \wedge q)$	[Ident

Example 2

$$[(P \cap Q) \cup (P' \cap Q')]' = (Q' \cap P) \cup (P' \cap Q)$$

Proof

$[(P \cap Q) \cup (P' \cap Q')]'$

$= (P \cap Q)' \cap (P' \cap Q')'$	[De M
$= (P' \cup Q') \cap (P \cup Q)$	[De M, Inv
$= [(P' \cup Q') \cap P] \cup [(P' \cup Q') \cap Q]$	[Distr
$= (P' \cap P) \cup (Q' \cap P) \cup (P' \cap Q) \cup (Q' \cap Q)$	[Distr
$= \emptyset \cup (Q' \cap P) \cup (P' \cap Q) \cup \emptyset$	[Comp
$= (Q' \cap P) \cup (P' \cap Q)$	[Ident

As these examples illustrate, all of the algebraic techniques at one's disposal in the algebra of statements may be carried over to the algebra of sets, merely by making suitable adjustments to conform to the notational differences. From a conceptual point of view these two algebras have little or nothing in common; from a formal, or manipulative, point of view they are essentially identical. Here is one place where mathematical abstraction "pays off": emphasizing the "formalities" at the expense of "meanings" we recognize that in two entirely different contexts we are actually doing the same thing.

There are a couple of omissions in our discussion of the correspondence between the two algebras: What is the analogue in the statement algebra of the inclusion relation $\subseteq$? What is the analogue in the set algebra of the implication operation $\Rightarrow$? One is a relation while the other is an operation, so they are certainly not analogues of one another. We leave the answer to one of these questions as an exercise. The other will be considered in the next section.

EXERCISES

1. Since $p \Rightarrow q$ is an abbreviation for $\tilde{p} \vee q$, its analogue in terms of sets is $P' \cup Q$.
   (a) Write set analogues for the equivalences E-1, ..., E-11, listed at the end of Section 4, Chapter 1. Some of these analogues were proved as theorems or left as exercises in this section; identify these and give proofs for each of the others.
   (b) In the algebra of statements the assertion *form A is a tautology* means $A \equiv I$. State and prove the set analogues of each of the tautologies T-1, ..., T-11 listed at the end of Section 4, Chapter 1.

2. We have seen (Theorems 2, 4) that:

$$\text{If } P = Q, \text{ then } P \cup R = Q \cup R.$$
$$\text{If } P = Q, \text{ then } P \cap R = Q \cap R.$$

The converses of these theorems ("cancellation") fail unless $U = \emptyset$. For counterexamples take $P = U$, $Q = \emptyset$, and $U \neq \emptyset$. Then $P \neq Q$, but

$$P \cup R = Q \cup R \quad \text{if} \quad R = U$$

and

$$P \cap R = Q \cap R \quad \text{if} \quad R = \emptyset.$$

However, prove the following theorem:

$$\text{If } P \cup R = Q \cup R \text{ and } P \cap R = Q \cap R, \text{ then } P = Q.$$

Hint

$$
\begin{aligned}
P &= P \cup (P \cap R) & [? \\
&= P \cup (Q \cap R) & [? \\
&= (P \cup Q) \cap (P \cup R) & [? \\
&= (P \cup Q) \cap (Q \cup R) & [? \\
&= \; ?
\end{aligned}
$$

3. If A and B are subsets of U, and A is a subset of B, suppose X is any set "between" A and B:

$$A \subseteq X \subseteq B.$$

   Let $Y_1 = (A \cup X') \cap B$, $Y_2 = A \cup (X' \cap B)$, and prove
   (a) $Y_1 \cap X = A$ and $X \cup Y_2 = B$,
   (b) Y_1 and Y_2 are between A and B,
   (c) $Y_1 = Y_2$.

4. In the previous problem we can drop the subscripts, writing Y for both Y_1 and Y_2. Suppose that Z is any subset of U satisfying $X \cap Z = A$ and $X \cup Z = B$. Prove
   (a) Z is between A and B,
   (b) $Y = Z$.

5. Use the theorem in Exercise 2, above, to prove that neither of the lattices in Exercise 6, page 63, has property (vii).

6. Prove that the lattice diagrammed below does not have property (vii).

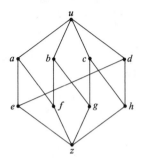

7. (a) Use distributivity (among other things) to simplify

$$[(P \cap Q) \cup (P \cap R)] \cap [(P \cap Q) \cup (Q \cap R)].$$

(b) Obtain the same result, using only consequences of properties (i) through (vi).

4. THE "IDENTITY" OF THE TWO ALGEBRAS

In Section 3 we proved a number of theorems of set algebra. In Chapter 3 we shall use the results obtained in Section 3 to study sentence structure and to extend our analysis of mathematical reasoning. However, the proofs we gave in Section 3 are themselves examples of mathematical reasoning of a particular kind. In this section we examine some of those proofs critically and show how they may be analyzed using only the primitive theory of inference outlined in Chapter 1.

Thus we apply our algebra of statements to analyze our algebra of sets. In the latter part of this section we shall turn the tables and use our algebra of sets for an analysis of our algebra of statements.

Analysis of Proofs in The Algebra of Sets

In Chapter 1 we gave no definitions for the terms *statement*, *true*, and *false*. Indeed, our statement algebra is itself an abstract system, so that all that we have had to say about abstract systems so far in this chapter applies as well to the algebra of statements as to the algebra of sets. We shall see, indeed, that our set algebra provides an interpretation, or a model, of our statement algebra. We do this, as might be expected, by assigning the terms *statement*, *true*, and *false* to certain expressions which occur in set algebra. As we must always do when "interpreting" an abstract system, we encounter the question of seeing that our interpretation "fits." In this case, we have

to convince ourselves that the laws of the excluded middle and of contradiction are satisfied.

If we examine the syntax of our set algebra we find that each of the seven
fundamental properties, and all of the consequences derived from them, are
constructed from expressions like $P \subseteq Q$ and $P = Q$ using the connectives
and, or, not, and *if*:

First we have the "nouns": $\emptyset$, U, P, Q, $P \cup Q$, $P \cap Q$, P', and some
more involved combinations, like

$$P \cap (Q \cup R), \quad (P \cap Q)', \quad P \cap (Q \cap R) \cap (P' \cap R'), \quad \text{etc.}$$

Each such expression represents a subset of U.

Next we have what we shall call *atomic statements*:

$$P = Q, \quad P \subseteq Q, \quad P \neq Q, \quad P \nsubseteq Q,$$

where now P and Q represent any nouns, like those mentioned in the previous
sentence.

Finally, each atomic statement and any combination of atomic statements
formed, in the "usual" way, with the connectives *and, or, not,* and *if* we shall
call a *statement* of set algebra.

Having made an agreement on what a "statement" is to be, we now must
decide which ones should be "true" and which "false." Again, we consider
atomic statements first. We are to split the class of all statements into two
mutually exclusive and mutually exhaustive parts: the statements in one of
these parts to be called *true statements* and those in the other to be called
false statements. We have considerable latitude in deciding which atomic
statements go into each part: indeed all we need require is that exactly one
of each pair $P = Q$, $P \neq Q$ and exactly one of each pair $P \subseteq Q$, $P \nsubseteq Q$
go into each part. If we identify $\sim(P = Q)$ with $P \neq Q$, $\sim(P \neq Q)$ with
$P = Q$, $\sim(P \subseteq Q)$ with $P \nsubseteq Q$, and $\sim(P \nsubseteq Q)$ with $P \subseteq Q$, a glance
at the truth table for negation given in Chapter 1 shows that the laws of the
excluded middle and of contradiction are satisfied by the classification
scheme just described: each atomic statement is either true or false and no
atomic statement is both true and false.

Before we classify compound statements we consider briefly where we
stand. We have two classes of atomic statements: those in one class we call
true atomic statements and those in the other *false* atomic statements. But
which is which, and what is the difference? It doesn't matter! And it is
important that it does not. Our set algebra is itself abstract and must en-
compass a great variety of specific instances. For example, perhaps $U = \emptyset$,
or perhaps $U \neq \emptyset$; at least one or the other, but not both—which, we
are not entitled to say unless we assume more than we have a right to assume.

Whether or not a given atomic statement is "true" is itself a matter of interpretation.

We use the truth tables in Chapter 1 to classify nonatomic statements as *true* or *false*. The tables make these decisions depend on the classification of the atomic statements from which a compound statement is constructed. Now each entry in each of these tables is either T or F and there are no blanks in any of the tables, nor are there any spaces with both a T and an F. It follows that the laws of the excluded middle and of contradiction are still in force. Hence the algebra of sets provides a model for the algebra of statements.

In terms of this model the proofs in Section 3 can be analyzed as follows. Take properties (i) through (vii), and everything that can be obtained from them by specialization, as "premises." The theorems and the results left as exercises in Section 3 represent "conclusions" which may be drawn from these premises by "chains of inferences." We give some examples, by way of illustration, and leave quite a few exercises.

Theorem 2(1) $P \subseteq P \cup Q$ and $Q \subseteq P \cup Q$.

Proof

(1) $P \cup Q \subseteq P \cup Q$ [(i) with $P \cup Q$ for P

(2) $(P \cup Q \subseteq P \cup Q) \Rightarrow (P \subseteq P \cup Q) \wedge (Q \subseteq P \cup Q)$

                                         [(v) with $P \cup Q$ for R

(3) $\therefore$ $(P \subseteq P \cup Q) \wedge (Q \subseteq P \cup Q)$ [(1), (2); $p \wedge (p \Rightarrow q) \Rightarrow q$

Theorem 2(2)   If $P \subseteq Q$, then $P \cup R \subseteq Q \cup R$.

Proof. Assume $P \subseteq Q$. To deduce $P \cup R \subseteq Q \cup R$.

(1) $P \subseteq Q$ [Hyp

(2) $Q \subseteq Q \cup R$ [Th 2(1)

(3) $(P \subseteq Q) \wedge (Q \subseteq Q \cup R) \Rightarrow (P \subseteq Q \cup R)$

                                         [(ii): $Q \cup R$ for R

(4) $\therefore$ $P \subseteq Q \cup R$ [(1), (2), (3). (T-4)

(5) $R \subseteq Q \cup R$ [Th 2(1)

(6) $(P \subseteq Q \cup R) \wedge (R \subseteq Q \cup R) \Rightarrow (P \cup R \subseteq Q \cup R)$

                                         [(v): R for Q, $Q \cup R$ for R

(7) $\therefore$ $P \cup R \subseteq Q \cup R$ Q.E.D.   [(4), (5), (6). (T-4)

We could go on like this, but resist the temptation; leaving other examples as exercises for those interested.

When it comes to proofs, there are two problems: (1) How do you recognize a proof when you see one? (2) How do you find one in the first place? Neither question is easily answered—as one might expect unless he believes mathematics is completely trivial. It is the purpose of logic to throw light on the first question, and thus indirectly on the second; finding proofs presumably requires an ability to recognize them. People who are good at constructing proofs are often said to be "mathematically mature," which may be only a way of saying that how they get that way is a mystery. Practice sometimes helps, and may be indispensable; it is often prescribed.

Boolean Algebras

We saw in Section 3 that the basic laws of the algebra of statements are all theorems of the algebra of sets. We have seen in this section that our set algebra is an "instance" or a "model" of our statement algebra. We now complete the identification by showing that our statement algebra is an "instance" of our set algebra. The common structure of these two systems is described by saying that each is a *Boolean algebra*. The name honors George Boole (1815–1864), a brilliant Irish mathematician credited with the creation of the modern algebraic treatment of logic.

A Boolean algebra is a "system" with two binary operations (*and, or*, or *intersection, union*, in our cases) each of which has an *identity* (I and O, or U and $\emptyset$), a unary operation (*not*, or *complement*), and two binary relations (*equivalence, equality*, and also, for sets at least, *inclusion*) satisfying all the various laws, theorems, and properties, we have discussed. Our identification will be completed by finding in our algebra of statements an analogue for set inclusion, and by showing that properties (i) through (vii) hold. Finally, after that is done, we examine Stone's theorem for our statement algebra: it turns out to throw some light on the place of truth tables in the algebra of Chapter 1.

The fundamental entities of our statement algebra are the so-called *forms*:

$$p, \quad p \wedge q, \quad p \Rightarrow q, \quad p \vee (p \wedge q), \quad \text{etc.}$$

The basic laws are relations of equivalence between forms:

$$p \wedge q \equiv q \wedge p, \quad p \vee (q \vee r) \equiv (p \vee q) \vee r, \quad \text{etc.}$$

Another relation between forms, which in fact served as the foundation for our theory of inference, is that of "tautological implication." If A and B are forms and $A \Rightarrow B$ is a tautology, we say that A *tautologically implies* B. In this case, let us write $A \leq B$. Thus $A \leq B$ and $(A \Rightarrow B) \equiv I$ are merely different ways of expressing the same relation.

As the notation suggests we have proposed a candidate for the analogue of the relation of set inclusion. We must now check properties (i) through (vii):

(i) $A \leq A$, for any form A: $A \Rightarrow A$ is a tautology; it can be obtained from the tautology $p \Rightarrow p$ by specialization.

(ii) If $A \leq B$ and $B \leq C$, then $A \leq C$. Suppose

$$(A \Rightarrow B) \equiv I \quad \text{and} \quad (B \Rightarrow C) \equiv I,$$

then

$$(A \Rightarrow B) \wedge (B \Rightarrow C) \equiv I;$$

but

$$(A \Rightarrow B) \wedge (B \Rightarrow C) \Rightarrow (A \Rightarrow C) \equiv I,$$

so

$$I \Rightarrow (A \Rightarrow C) \equiv I.$$

Finally

$$I \Rightarrow (A \Rightarrow C) \equiv A \Rightarrow C.$$

(iii) $A \leq B$ and $B \leq A$ if and only if $A \equiv B$. Here

$$A \Leftrightarrow B \equiv (A \Rightarrow B) \wedge (B \Rightarrow A)$$

so

$$(A \Leftrightarrow B) \equiv I$$

if and only if

$$(A \Rightarrow B) \wedge (B \Rightarrow A) \equiv I,$$

which certainly holds if both $(A \Rightarrow B) \equiv I$ and $(B \Rightarrow A) \equiv I$, but not otherwise.

(iv) $O \leq A$ and $A \leq I$; that is, $(O \Rightarrow A) \equiv I$ and $(A \Rightarrow I) \equiv I$, or $I \vee A \equiv I$ and $(\sim A) \vee I \equiv I$, respectively.

(v) $A \leq C$ and $B \leq C$ if and only if $A \vee B \leq C$. Suppose

$$(A \Rightarrow C) \equiv I \quad \text{and} \quad (B \Rightarrow C) \equiv I.$$

Then

$$(A \Rightarrow C) \wedge (B \Rightarrow C) \equiv I,$$

but $(A \Rightarrow C) \wedge (B \Rightarrow C) \equiv (A \vee B \Rightarrow C)$, by E-11, and conversely.

(vi) $C \leq A$ and $C \leq B$ if and only if $C \leq A \wedge B$. Similar to (v): cf. E-8.

(vii) $A \wedge (\sim B) \equiv O$ if and only if $A \leq B$. This is the easiest of all: $A \wedge (\sim B) \equiv O$ if and only if $(\sim A) \vee B \equiv I$.

In Section 3 we deduced the "basic laws" from (i) through (vii); here we have just gone the other way. Thus neither list has any consequence that the other does not also have.

To verify Stone's theorem we are obliged to find sets of some kind to represent our forms in such a way that one is a subset of another if the form represented by the first tautologically implies that represented by the second. For this project we must be rather more precise than we have been up to now.

There is not just one statement algebra, there are infinitely many: they differ in the number of symbols each involves, which may be any given positive number—integral, of course. Thus we may consider the algebra S_2 with two symbols (say, p and q), or the algebra S_3 with three (p, q, r), or indeed S_n, where n is any positive integer. In Chapter 1 we were vague about these distinctions, which are reflected there in the length of our truth tables. The fact is that for each n the system S_n is a Boolean algebra. (In S_n the table for each form has 2^n rows.)

A representation of S_n, of the kind required in Stone's theorem, can be obtained by selecting for each form just those rows in its table which contain T's. For example ($n = 2$), $p \vee q$ can be represented by rows 1, 2, 3; $p \wedge q$ by row 1 only; etc. For the sets, we simply take these collections of rows. Note that if $A \leq B$, the set of rows containing T's in the table for A is a subset of the corresponding set of rows for B, and conversely. Thus (with $n = 2$, again) $p \wedge q \leq p \vee q$, that is, $\{1\} \subseteq \{1, 2, 3\}$. The form O (contradiction), of course, is represented by the void set $\emptyset$.

Disjunctive Normal Form

Our discussion of the representation just described can be recast in a manner which avoids reference to truth tables, and leads to a purely "mechanical" algebraic procedure for doing anything one can do with truth tables: proving equivalences, and establishing tautologies, for example.

Take $n = 2$ first, and consider the four forms:

$$p \wedge q, \quad p \wedge \bar{q}, \quad \bar{p} \wedge q, \quad \bar{p} \wedge \bar{q},$$

which we shall call *elementary* forms. The table for each of these elementary forms has exactly one T in it: in row 1, 2, 3, 4, respectively. Thus any form in two symbols can be "represented" by a subset of the set of our four elementary forms. As a matter of fact, any form, except O, is equivalent to the disjunction of the forms belonging to the subset which represents it. For example

$$p \vee q \equiv (p \wedge q) \vee (p \wedge \bar{q}) \vee (\bar{p} \wedge q),$$

and similarly for other forms involving p, q.

For $n = 3$ the elementary forms, corresponding to the four above in the case $n = 2$, are eight in number:

$$p \wedge q \wedge r, \quad p \wedge q \wedge \bar{r}, \quad \ldots, \quad \bar{p} \wedge \bar{q} \wedge \bar{r}.$$

And, in general, S_n has 2^n elementary forms: each is the conjunction of all n of the symbols. These elementary forms differ from one another in the 2^n

different ways it is possible to attach negation signs to the symbols: each has a truth table with exactly one T, all the other entries being F.

For brevity, let us write, at least temporarily,

$$p q r, \quad p q \bar{r}, \quad \ldots, \quad \bar{p} \bar{q} \bar{r},$$

instead of

$$p \wedge q \wedge r, \quad p \wedge q \wedge \bar{r}, \quad \ldots, \quad \bar{p} \wedge \bar{q} \wedge \bar{r},$$

for our elementary forms. As observed above, any given form is the disjunction of those elementary forms in the subset of all elementary forms which represents the given form. Thus, for another example, in S_3,

$$p \vee q \vee r \equiv p q r \vee p q \bar{r} \vee p \bar{q} r \vee p \bar{q} \bar{r} \vee \bar{p} q r \vee \bar{p} \bar{q} r \vee \bar{p} \bar{q} r.$$

Such a representation of a form, as a disjunction of elementary forms, is called a representation in *disjunctive normal form*. The disjunctive normal form of a given form is uniquely determined once n, the number of symbols, is specified. Of course n cannot be less than the number of symbols which actually appear in the given form.

Thus the normal form of p in S_1 is p itself; in S_2 the normal form of p is $p q \vee p \bar{q}$; in S_3 it is $p q r \vee p q \bar{r} \vee p \bar{q} r \vee p \bar{q} \bar{r}$; etc. Such expansions can be obtained "simply" by "multiplying" the given form by the tautology $(p \vee \bar{p})(q \vee \bar{q}) \ldots$, with enough factors to include all the required symbols, and by "multiplying out" all the parentheses. Finally one drops self-contradictory terms and duplicates. For $n = 2$ and symbols p, q, for example,

$$
\begin{aligned}
p \Rightarrow q &\equiv \bar{p} \vee q \\
&\equiv (\bar{p} \vee q)(p \vee \bar{p})(q \vee \bar{q}) \\
&\equiv (\bar{p} \vee q)(p q \vee p \bar{q} \vee \bar{p} q \vee \bar{p} \bar{q}) \\
&\equiv \bar{p} p q \vee \bar{p} p \bar{q} \vee \bar{p} \bar{p} q \vee \bar{p} \bar{p} \bar{q} \vee p q q \vee p q \bar{q} \vee \bar{p} q q \vee \bar{p} q \bar{q} \\
&\equiv p q \vee \bar{p} q \vee \bar{p} \bar{q}.
\end{aligned}
$$

Here $\bar{p} p q$, $\bar{p} p \bar{q}$, $p q \bar{q}$, $\bar{p} q \bar{q}$ are self-contradictory, while $\bar{p} \bar{p} q$ duplicates $\bar{p} q q$. The result should surprise nobody who knows the truth table for $p \Rightarrow q$. The point here is that the completely "mechanical" process of constructing truth tables can be replaced by a completely "mechanical" algebraic procedure. Each of these "mechanical" methods is quite capable of being handled satisfactorily by a suitably constructed automatic machine and also, one might imagine, by a child or a chimpanzee, provided he has a set of certain rather well-defined reflexes.

Some electrical engineers are particularly fascinated by disjunctive normal forms—why, one might imagine by looking again at the circuits for the voting and adding machines in Chapter 1, Section 5. The calculations we used to simplify those circuits are just the reverse of the calculation above for reduction to normal form.

EXERCISES

1. Assign each of the sixteen compound forms discussed on page 14 to the points in the Hasse diagram (page 57) for the subsets of a four-element set, in such a way that one form is joined to another below it if and only if the higher one implies the lower one tautologically. (Write $p \Leftrightarrow q$ and $\sim(p \Leftrightarrow q)$ instead of $\sim(p \veebar q)$ and $p \veebar q$, respectively.)

2. By finding the disjunctive normal form of each side, prove the following equivalence:

$$(p \Rightarrow q) \wedge (q \Rightarrow r) \wedge (r \Rightarrow p) \equiv (r \Rightarrow q) \wedge (q \Rightarrow p) \wedge (p \Rightarrow r).$$

CHAPTER THREE

SENTENCE STRUCTURE AND INFERENCE

In this chapter we discuss the internal structure of "atomic" statements and consider relations between statements (in particular, deducibility) which depend on questions of internal structure.

It may reasonably be expected that the task we now set for ourselves is more complicated than any we have undertaken so far. In Chapter 1, for example, we had a "formal system" (our algebra of statements) whose "interpretation" (given by truth tables) was extremely simple. In Chapter 2 we had more or less the same formal system but with a different interpretation. In this chapter we shall also be concerned with a "system" and with its "interpretation"; we shall, however, treat the system rather informally, by comparison with our previous work.

We shall be concerned with *conditions*, or *predicates*, *relations*, and *quantifiers* and we shall devote a good deal of attention to "tautologies" involving them. We shall be able to carry over, or adapt, many of the ideas and techniques we used in Chapter 1. But we shall make no serious attempt to construct our system formally, as we did in Chapter 1, by assembling "basic laws," "derivation rules," or the like. In Chapter 1 the "basic laws" were shown to hold for the interpretation we gave for them using truth tables. The other tautologies we got from the basic laws using the technique of "algebraic derivation."

Here we extend the meaning of the term *tautology*, justify some of our new tautologies by considering their interpretation, and show how others may be obtained by deductive techniques from ones previously justified. But we shall not even purport to provide any kind of basic list of such tautologies. The algebra in Chapter 1 was interpreted using truth tables. The "system" discussed in this chapter will be interpreted using the algebra of sets constructed in Chapter 2.

Our first item of business is to consider "conditions."

Conditions

In the "locus problems" of elementary geometry one is given some "condition" and asked to determine the "locus" of points "satisfying" the given condition. A "locus" is just a subset of some universe, often the set of points in a plane, or in space. Typical of these problems is: given a pair of distinct points a, b, determine the locus of points closer to a than to b. The problem is to describe the set containing all such points and no others. (The answer, of course, is the set of all points lying on that side of the perpendicular bisector of segment ab which contains the point a.) Such problems illustrate the idea that a "condition" which may be imposed on the members of a given universe singles out a certain subset of the universe—that subset whose elements are all members of the universe which "satisfy" the condition.

Viewed abstractly, there is no difference between the locus problems of geometry and the algebraic problems involved in "solving equations." Given an equation, for example,

$$x^3 - 3x^2 + 2x = 0,$$

and a universe U, e.g., the set of rational numbers, find the subset of U whose members are the "solutions" of the given equation. (In our example, the set of solutions is $\{0, 1, 2\}$.) Equations involving an "unknown" x are often described as expressing a "condition on x"; though, even in algebra, one also encounters many "conditions" expressed in other ways. Some, like the condition that a quadratic equation have real roots, are given by inequalities.

The examples we have mentioned, and many others of a similar nature, suggest the general principle that, given a universe U and given a condition, the condition "singles out," or "specifies," a certain subset of U: that subset whose members are all members of U satisfying the given condition. This principle is called the *principle of specification*; it expresses a fundamental relation between sets and conditions, and is the basic idea behind the application of set algebra to the study of sentence structure. The subset of U specified by a given condition is called the *extension* of that condition in U.

Given a universe U and given a condition, the specification principle asserts that U contains a subset which is the extension of the given condition in U. On the other hand, given the universe U and given any subset A of U, we may say that there is some condition whose extension in U is A. One such condition is that of "belonging to A"; often in specific cases it is possible to give less "trivial" examples of conditions having prescribed extensions. We conclude that each condition is paired with some subset of U and each subset of U is paired with at least one condition. Conditions having the same extension in U are said to be *equivalent* or, more precisely, *equivalent relative to U*. The procedure for solving equations or locus problems is exactly that of finding other conditions equivalent to given conditions (relative to whatever universe is involved).

In the interest of clarity, the description of a condition must be considered incomplete unless the relevant universe is carefully specified. Carelessness can result in ambiguity (perhaps harmless, but possibly serious) or in chaos. We illustrate these possibilities with some examples.

1. Harmless ambiguity: The locus problem mentioned at the beginning of this section. The universe might be the set of points in a plane. Then the perpendicular bisector of segment ab is a line. But if the universe is the set of points in three-dimensional space, that bisector is a plane. In both of these cases the locus was correctly described, but it takes two proofs to show that it was.

2. Serious ambiguity: Consider the equation $2x - 1 = 0$. If U is the set of integers, the set of solutions is $\emptyset$; if U is the set of rational numbers, the set is $\{\frac{1}{2}\}$. Other examples are familiar to everyone: $x^2 - 2 = 0$ with U the rationals, the reals; $x^2 + 1 = 0$ with U the reals, the complexes; etc.

3. Chaos: Although conditions may be used to characterize or specify subsets of a given set, it is too much to expect that conditions or properties, by themselves, might be used for the "creation" of sets. The classic example of the fact that such extravagance may lead to disaster is due to Bertrand Russell. Consider the "innocent" condition of "being a set," and let A denote its extension. The members of A, then, are sets, and every set is a member of A. (We have already committed our crime by allowing the condition to "define" a set without first delimiting a universe containing its extension. But this once is enough; observe how much more carefully we use the specification principle in the next step!) Given A, we consider it as universe for the condition expressed by $x \notin x$, whose extension, in A, we shall call B. The new condition is quite reasonable too. As a matter of fact—though it is quite irrelevant—B is not void: $\emptyset$ is a set, and hence a member of A. But $\emptyset \notin \emptyset$, so $\emptyset$ satisfies the condition. Hence $\emptyset \in B$ and B has at least one member. Now B is a set; thus B is a member of A. Like Sophocles' *Oedipus*, we are compelled to ask one more question: B is a member of A as well as a subset of A; is it possible that B is also a member of B? If $B \in B$, then B is a member of the extension of $x \notin x$ and so satisfies the condition. Hence $B \notin B$. Contradiction. The only other possibility is $B \notin B$, and this also leads to a contradiction: if $B \notin B$, then B satisfies the condition and so is a member of its extension, $B \in B$. The trap has closed.

In the following pages we shall examine the way the term *existence* is used in mathematics. We shall see that saying something "exists" having certain properties or satisfying certain conditions means that, among the members of a *given* set, there is at least one satisfying the requirements. With some collection at hand we may use conditions to single out one or more members of the given collection. But no amount of ingenuity in manipulating conditions alone can produce something from nothing.

Conditions and their extensions are by no means peculiar to mathematics —they are fundamental epistemological and linguistic concepts. When a scientist discusses physical or chemical *properties* of substances he is talking about *conditions* as we have been using the word. Some organic compounds are volatile and others are not. Thus the property (or condition!) of volatility singles out a certain subset of the universe of organic compounds, those which are volatile. Grammarians refer to conditions as *predicates*. The predicate (or condition!) *mortal* singles out certain of the characters of mythology (for example): its extension is the set of mortals.

Open Sentences

In mathematics conditions are ordinarily expressed using "unknowns" or "variables." Thus *x is positive*, $x^3 - x^2 = 7$, *P is equidistant from a given point F and a given line d*, etc. Such expressions containing variables are called *open sentences*. If α is a condition on the universe U, we write $\alpha(x)$ for the corresponding open sentence, which we read: *x has property α* or *x satisfies condition α*. The letter x is called a *variable* and the universe U is called the *domain* of the variable x. If a is a member of U and if the variable x in the open sentence $\alpha(x)$ is replaced by a, the result is a statement $\alpha(a)$. A statement of the type $\alpha(a)$ is said to have *subject-predicate* form: a is its subject and α its predicate. In view of the definition of the extension of a condition, $\alpha(a)$ if and only if $a \in A$, provided A is the extension of α in U. Thus we may think of $\alpha(a)$ and $a \in A$ as merely different ways of "expressing the same statement."

The process of replacing the variable x in an open sentence $\alpha(x)$ by the name of a member of the domain of x is referred to as "closing the open sentence $\alpha(x)$"; the resulting statement, $\alpha(a)$, is called a *closed sentence*. (In Sections 1 and 4 we shall study other ways one may "close" open sentences.)

A word about the syntactical status of variables is in order. The letter x in an open sentence $\alpha(x)$ has the grammatical function of the blanks in oaths, deeds, promissory notes, and other forms. In particular x is not a name—it does not denote anything at all—it merely reserves a place which may be occupied by the name of some member of its domain. When such a blank is filled properly, the result is a statement. An open sentence by itself is grammatically incomplete; the process of "closing" it converts it into a statement.

So far we have mentioned three things: a condition (or predicate) α on U, the open sentence $\alpha(x)$, and a set—the extension of α in U. (Later on there will be a fourth, called a *graph* of α.) For some people this is too much. The idea is that such a multiplicity of concepts is extravagant and unnecessary, and therefore undesirable. Some mathematicians, for example, find the condition superfluous, and identify it either with the sentence or with the set.

Thus an equation or an inequality is an open sentence whose extension is its set of solutions: to imagine that some third entity (the condition) may be lurking around too is distasteful to many. Some therefore say the condition *is* the equation (or the inequality), and others say the condition *is* the set. (The latter, especially, if the condition happens to be a relation.)

Grammarians are not so parsimonious: as a matter of fact they prefer predicates to either open sentences or their extensions and rarely ever mention the latter.

Even if this difference in point of view should remind some of the medieval controversy between nominalists and realists, we shall not take the question too seriously. After all, a problem which can be avoided with a little circumlocution cannot be much of a problem. Indeed, we go so far as to indulge in the luxury of an "algebra of conditions," even though it amounts to a "carbon copy" of the algebras we already have.

Algebra of Conditions

Consider a universe U, fixed for this discussion. Suppose that α, β, γ, ... are conditions on U whose extensions in U are, respectively, A, B, C, ... We have already defined equivalence of a pair of conditions as meaning that their extensions are equal. Write $\alpha \equiv \beta$ if α, β are equivalent in this sense. We now look at some operations on conditions:

If α, β are given conditions, let $\alpha \vee \beta$ be a condition with extension $A \cup B$, let $\alpha \wedge \beta$ be a condition with extension $A \cap B$, and let $\tilde{\alpha}$ be a condition with extension A'.

It is a straightforward matter to verify that these definitions entail a number of results like

$$\alpha \vee \beta \equiv \beta \vee \alpha, \quad \alpha \wedge (\beta \wedge \gamma) \equiv (\alpha \wedge \beta) \wedge \gamma, \quad \sim(\tilde{\alpha}) \equiv \alpha,$$

etc., since

$$A \cup B = B \cup A, \quad A \cap (B \cap C) = (A \cap B) \cap C, \quad (A')' = A,$$

and so on. We leave as exercises some of the details of this algebra of conditions and turn instead to the open sentences corresponding to compound conditions.

Let us write

$$
\begin{array}{lll}
\alpha(x) \vee \beta(x) & \text{for} & (\alpha \vee \beta)(x), \\
\alpha(x) \wedge \beta(x) & \text{for} & (\alpha \wedge \beta)(x), \\
\sim\alpha(x), \text{ or } \tilde{\alpha}(x), & \text{for} & (\tilde{\alpha})(x)
\end{array}
$$

and agree to call the open sentence $\alpha(x) \vee \beta(x)$ the *disjunction* of the open sentences $\alpha(x)$, $\beta(x)$; $\alpha(x) \wedge \beta(x)$ their *conjunction*; and $\sim\alpha(x)$ the *negation* of $\alpha(x)$. Borrowing other notation from our statement algebra, we write

$$\alpha \Rightarrow \beta \qquad \text{for} \qquad \tilde{\alpha} \vee \beta$$

and

$$\alpha(x) \Rightarrow \beta(x) \qquad \text{for} \qquad (\alpha \Rightarrow \beta)(x),$$

and treat $\Leftrightarrow$ similarly.

Such definitions allow us to construct a "dictionary" for translating open sentences from our "set language" to our "condition language" and vice versa. Examples of pairs of entries in this dictionary are

$$\alpha(x) \leftrightarrow x \in A,$$
$$\alpha(x) \vee \beta(x) \leftrightarrow x \in A \cup B,$$
$$\alpha(x) \wedge \beta(x) \leftrightarrow x \in A \cap B,$$
$$\tilde{\alpha}(x) \leftrightarrow x \in A',$$
$$\alpha(x) \Rightarrow \beta(x) \leftrightarrow x \in A' \cup B,$$
$$\alpha(x) \Leftrightarrow \beta(x) \leftrightarrow x \in (A' \cup B) \cap (A \cup B').$$

We may even express the inclusion relation of our set algebra in terms of conditions: Let us write, say, $\alpha \leq \beta$ for $A \subseteq B$. If $\alpha \leq \beta$, we say that condition α is *sufficient* for condition β or that condition β is *necessary* for condition α. (Thus, for example, congruence is sufficient for similarity and similarity is necessary for congruence: for two triangles to be similar it is sufficient that they be congruent, and for two triangles to be congruent it is necessary that they be similar.) The relation $\leq$ is called the *implication-relation* for conditions (*condition α implies condition β*). Under no circumstances, however, may it be confused with the *implication-operation* $\alpha \Rightarrow \beta$, defined earlier. The expression $\alpha \Rightarrow \beta$ is a compound condition: namely, $\tilde{\alpha} \vee \beta$. On the other hand, $\alpha \leq \beta$ "says" something about conditions. The syntactical relation between the expressions $\alpha \Rightarrow \beta$ and $\alpha \leq \beta$ corresponds to that between a noun and a sentence: the former is a name of a condition, the latter asserts something about a pair of conditions.

As with sets and statements, we can introduce "symbolic conditions," say π, ρ, σ, etc., and develop an algebra of conditions. The laws of this algebra, for example,

$$\pi \vee \rho \equiv \rho \vee \pi, \qquad \pi \wedge (\rho \vee \sigma) \equiv (\pi \wedge \rho) \vee (\pi \wedge \sigma), \qquad \text{etc.,}$$

are easily obtained from the laws of set algebra, using the definitions given above for $\vee$, $\wedge$, $\sim$, $\leq$, $\equiv$ in terms of the corresponding set operations and relations. (This is just a matter of some rewriting, and is left as an exercise.) Associated with each symbolic condition on U is its symbolic extension in U. Two pieces of notation are used to indicate the association between conditions and their extensions. Thus if π represents a condition on U and P its extension in U, we write either

$$P = \text{Ext } \pi \qquad \text{or} \qquad P = \{x \in U : \pi(x)\},$$

depending on which seems more convenient at the moment. The former is more concise than the latter, but forces one to examine the context to find out what U is.

EXERCISES

1. Translate the set properties (i) through (vii) into the language of conditions. Write O for a condition with extension $\varnothing$ and I for a condition with extension U.

2. Rewrite the basic laws (Section 2, Chapter 1) and the equivalences E-1, ..., E-11 (Section 4, Chapter 1) with condition symbols π, ρ, σ in place of p, q, r. Explain why the resulting assertions hold, no matter what the universe U may be.

3. Define two new operations on conditions as follows:

$$\pi - \rho = \pi \wedge \tilde{\rho} \qquad \text{(``subtraction''),}$$
$$\pi + \rho = (\pi - \rho) \vee (\rho - \pi) \qquad \text{(``addition'').}$$

Prove that addition is both commutative and associative, but that subtraction is neither commutative nor associative; that

$$\pi \equiv \rho \qquad \text{if and only if} \qquad \pi + \rho \equiv O$$

and

$$\pi \wedge (\rho + \sigma) \equiv (\pi \wedge \rho) + (\pi \wedge \sigma).$$

Find the analogues of addition and subtraction in the algebras of statements and of sets.

1. QUANTIFIERS

We have referred to open sentences and mentioned one way they may be "closed": replacing the variable by the name of a member of its domain converts an open sentence into a statement having subject-predicate form. In this section we consider two more ways an open sentence may be closed. In Section 4 we shall examine some open sentences of a special kind and find that they may be closed in still other ways. All of the methods we now examine involve the use of so-called *quantifiers*.

For our work in Sections 1 through 3 we make no special assumptions about the universe U, except for an occasional restriction to cases in which U is not "too small." (For example, $U \neq \varnothing$.) In Section 4, however, we make very definite restrictive assumptions on the universe. (We assume it can be "factored" into a "product" of two sets.) Although what we do in Sections 1 through 3 carries over to the special cases we examine later, what we do in Section 4 cannot be applied to the more general case which we discuss first.

There are two main quantifiers. They are known as the *universal quantifier* and the *existential quantifier*. We examine each in turn and later investigate their connection with each other.

Universal Quantifier

Suppose α is a condition on the universe U and that the extension of α in U is A. Unless $U = \emptyset$, there are two possibilities: either $A = U$ or $A \neq U$. In terms of the open sentence $\alpha(x)$, we express the first alternative by writing

$$(\forall x \in U)\alpha(x).$$

The prefix, $(\forall x \in U)$, is called a *universal quantifier*; it may be read *for each x in U, for every x in U, for all x in U*, etc. The entire expression represents the statement *Every member of U satisfies condition α*. In a context in which there can be no confusion about what is the universe, $(\forall x \in U)\alpha(x)$ is often abbreviated to $(\forall x)\alpha(x)$, and sometimes even to $(x)\alpha(x)$.

Some examples of statements having the form $(\forall x \in U)\alpha(x)$ are

All men are mortal.

(U the set of men, α the predicate *mortal*) and

Congruent triangles are similar.

(U the set of *pairs* of triangles and α the predicate $\beta \Rightarrow \gamma$, where β is the predicate *congruent* and γ is the predicate *similar*.) The apparently more intricate structure of the latter example may be exhibited by writing

$$(\forall x \in U)[\beta(x) \Rightarrow \gamma(x)],$$

whose translation in set language is

$$B' \cup C = U$$

if B, C, respectively, are the extensions of β, γ in U. In view of Exercise 4, page 69, another version is $B \subseteq C$: the set of all pairs of congruent triangles is a subset of the set of all pairs of similar triangles.

Our two examples are not as different as the analyses just given may seem to indicate. If we change the universe in the second example to the set of pairs of congruent triangles, we may write simply $(\forall x \in U)\gamma(x)$. And in the first example, if we take U as the set of people, we can write $(\forall x \in U)[\beta(x) \Rightarrow \alpha(x)]$, if $\beta(x)$ represents the open sentence x *is a man*. Then, as above, another version of the first is: the set of men is a subset of the set of mortals. These differences are a matter of refining the analysis and do not represent any intrinsic difference between the given statements. Indeed, we have just seen that these two statements have essentially the same structure. In Section 3 we shall have more to say about how the choice of universe affects the parsing of statements like these.

Other examples of statements having the form $(\forall x \in U)\alpha(x)$ are provided by the identities of algebra and "trigonometry":

$$x^2 - 1 = (x - 1)(x + 1),$$
$$\sin^2 x + \cos^2 x = 1,$$

etc. If $\alpha(x)$ represents such an "equality," then the claim that $\alpha(x)$ is an identity is precisely the assertion $(\forall x \in U)\alpha(x)$, where U is whatever universe is relevant (e.g., the set of real numbers).

Existential Quantifier

If α is a condition on U and A is the extension of α in U, we write

$$(\exists x \in U)\alpha(x)$$

for $A \neq \varnothing$. The prefix, $(\exists x \in U)$, is called an *existential quantifier*; it may be read *for at least one x in U, for some x in U, there is an x in U for which, there exists an x in U such that*, etc. When there is no danger of confusion, $(\exists x \in U)$ may be abbreviated to $(\exists x)$.

Examples

Something is rotten in the state of Denmark.

(U: things in Denmark, α: rotten.)

Some numbers are positive.

(U: numbers, α: positive.)

England has a queen.

(U: the set of people in England, $\alpha(x)$: *x is a queen*. This example is ambiguous: a different way to interpret it is obtained by letting U represent the set of people, with $\alpha(x)$ for *x is queen of England*.)

Somebody ate my porridge.

(U: the set of living beings, including—for the benefit of quibblers—characters of fiction, $\alpha(x)$: *x ate my porridge*.)

Other examples of existential statements are provided by assertions that an equation has at least one solution of some sort:

$$2x^2 + x - 1 = 0 \quad \textit{has an integral root.}$$
$$x^2 - 2 = 0 \quad \textit{has a real root.}$$

or that there is some geometrical object with certain properties:

A circle may be inscribed in a given triangle.

The medians of a given triangle are concurrent.

(Here we interpret the last example as saying that there is some point common to all the medians.)

We now have three ways to close an open sentence:

$$\alpha(a), \qquad (\forall x \in U)\alpha(x), \qquad (\exists x \in U)\alpha(x).$$

Statements having the second and third forms are called *universal statements* and *existential statements*, respectively, in order to distinguish their structure from that of statements of the first kind which we have already described as having *subject-predicate* form.

The open sentence to which a quantifier is "applied" is called the *scope* of the quantifier. Thus, in $(\forall x \in U)\alpha(x)$, $\alpha(x)$ is the scope of $(\forall x \in U)$; and in $(\exists x \in U)[\alpha(x) \wedge \beta(x)] \Rightarrow (\forall x \in U)\gamma(x)$, $\alpha(x) \wedge \beta(x)$ is the scope of $(\exists x \in U)$. Many authors, but by no means all, define the scope of a quantifier so that the quantifier itself is a part of its scope; we prefer not to do this, for reasons which we trust will become apparent later.

In order to analyze a statement, one first has to assign it a "meaning." This act is called *interpretation*. Statements capable of being assigned different meanings are said to be *ambiguous*. It is important to learn to recognize ambiguities, for there are times when they should be avoided and other times when they can be exploited, depending on how one wishes to be interpreted.

One is assisted in the act of interpretation by his previous experience and by context. Anybody who has studied geometry knows that the difference between the statements

Equilateral triangles are isosceles.

Congruent triangles are similar.

is much greater than it may seem to someone who doesn't know the meaning of the words.

But even after a decision is made on the meaning of a statement, often there are still some choices to be made on how to parse it. For example, we have already analyzed the statement about congruent triangles in two ways; in Section 4 we shall do it in still another way.

EXERCISES

Analyze the structure of each of the following sentences using conditions and quantifiers on appropriate universes. (The form of your answer may depend on the universe you choose.) If a sentence is ambiguous, it can be parsed in a variety of ways.

1. Some reformers are dreamers.
2. Some sea serpents are not mammals.
3. All mammals make nice pets.
4. Some saber-tooth tigers are hard to tame.
5. Not all politicians are diplomats.
6. Not all diplomats are politicians.
7. Some scoundrels are neither politicians nor diplomats.
8. All equilateral triangles are isosceles.
9. Some isosceles triangles are equilateral.
10. None but the brave deserve the fair.
11. Not everyone who prays is a Buddhist.
12. Everyone who prays is not an atheist.
13. Everything that glitters is not gold.
14. All that glitters is not gold.
15. Some thing that glitters is not gold.
16. Something that glitters is not gold.
17. Some continuous functions are bounded.
18. Some bounded functions are integrable.
19. If a function is bounded and continuous, it is integrable.
20. If Shakespeare wrote any of Marlowe's plays, then some of Marlowe's plays are good.
21. If Jones is a scoundrel, then no one can be trusted.
22. If one apple is rotten, then all are.
23. He who hesitates is lost.
24. If he who hesitates is lost, then all are lost if all hesitate.
25. If there are criminals, there are police.
26. If it is the case that there are police if there are criminals, then there are some who would be police if they were criminals.
27. Some cops would be crooks if all cops were politicians.
28. If the assumption that some cops were crooks implied that all cops were politicians, then all cops who were crooks would be politicians.

Special Cases: Finite Universe

Some writers refer to universal and existential statements as *general conjunctions* and *general disjunctions*, respectively. To see why, we examine some special cases. Suppose U is a finite set: for example,

$$U = \{a_1, a_2, \ldots, a_n\},$$

where n is a positive integer. Then both

$$(\forall x \in U)\alpha(x) \quad \text{and} \quad \alpha(a_1) \wedge \alpha(a_2) \wedge \cdots \wedge \alpha(a_n)$$

are true if $\alpha(a_1)$, $\alpha(a_2)$, . . . , $\alpha(a_n)$ are all true and false if at least one of $\alpha(a_1)$, $\alpha(a_2)$, . . . , $\alpha(a_n)$ is false. Similarly for

$$(\exists x \in U)\alpha(x)$$

and

$$\alpha(a_1) \vee \alpha(a_2) \vee \cdots \vee \alpha(a_n);$$

these are both true if at least one of $\alpha(a_1)$, $\alpha(a_2)$, . . . , $\alpha(a_n)$ is true and both are false if all of $\alpha(a_1)$, $\alpha(a_2)$, . . . , $\alpha(a_n)$ are false. Indeed, with any finite universe, one can get along without quantifiers: they may be replaced by conjunctions and disjunctions of statements having subject-predicate form. With an infinite universe, then, one may think of quantifiers as providing *bona fide* extensions of the notions of conjunction and disjunction to what could be called *infinite conjunctions* and *infinite disjunctions*. Thus there is an important distinction between what we are doing now and what we did in Chapter 1; a distinction illustrating rather emphatically just how feeble our algebra of statements is by comparison. Our algebra of sets is fundamental for carrying out this extension.

A couple of finite cases deserve particular mention, if only as curiosities. Suppose U is a singleton: say, $U = \{a\}$. Then

$$\alpha(a), \qquad (\forall x \in U)\alpha(x), \qquad (\exists x \in U)\alpha(x)$$

all amount to the same thing. Thus, for a universe with just one member (and only then!), every closed sentence has subject-predicate form.

Even more curious is the extreme case $U = \emptyset$. Here $\alpha(a)$ makes no sense because there is no member a of U. But $(\forall x \in U)\alpha(x)$ is just fine: in fact, it is true for any α. (If $A \subseteq U$ and $U = \emptyset$, then $A = \emptyset$, so $A = U$.) On the other hand $(\exists x \in U)\alpha(x)$ turns out to be false for any α. (As before $A = \emptyset$, so we cannot have $A \neq \emptyset$.) In this fascinating universe we have the following marvelous results: $\alpha \equiv \beta$ and $\alpha \equiv \sim\alpha$, for any conditions α, β. All conditions are equivalent and all general statements are true so long as one is talking about nothing, and only then; and just in this case all statements of existence are false.

"De Morgan's Laws"

Suppose U has just two members, say $U = \{a, b\}$. Then $(\forall x \in U)\alpha(x)$ and $(\exists x \in U)\alpha(x)$ represent

$$\alpha(a) \wedge \alpha(b)$$

and

$$\alpha(a) \vee \alpha(b),$$

respectively. Because of the De Morgan laws of Chapter 1,

$$\sim[\alpha(a) \wedge \alpha(b)] \Leftrightarrow \tilde{\alpha}(a) \vee \tilde{\alpha}(b)$$

and

$$\sim[\alpha(a) \lor \alpha(b)] \Leftrightarrow \tilde{\alpha}(a) \land \tilde{\alpha}(b)$$

are both formally true: each is true no matter what condition α may be. In Chapter 1 we defined tautologies in the algebra of statements; by analogy we shall call

$$\sim[\pi(a) \land \pi(b)] \Leftrightarrow \tilde{\pi}(a) \lor \tilde{\pi}(b)$$

and

$$\sim[\pi(a) \lor \pi(b)] \Leftrightarrow \tilde{\pi}(a) \land \tilde{\pi}(b)$$

tautologies: here π is a symbolic condition on U. We have just seen that replacing the free symbol π by any letter which represents a condition on U yields a true statement. Rewriting these tautologies with quantifiers, we have

$$\sim[(\forall x \in U)\pi(x)] \Leftrightarrow (\exists x \in U)\tilde{\pi}(x)$$

and

$$\sim[(\exists x \in U)\pi(x)] \Leftrightarrow (\forall x \in U)\tilde{\pi}(x).$$

We have proved these tautologies if U has two members. If U is void or a singleton their proofs are quite trivial. We could prove them for a finite universe with 3, or 4, or more, members easily enough; and, using mathematical induction, we could prove them for any finite universe. But simply by translating them into the language of sets we can justify these tautologies without any special assumptions on the size of U. Indeed, if P is the symbolic extension of π in U, translation converts them into

$$P \neq U \text{ if and only if } P' \neq \emptyset$$

and

$$P = \emptyset \text{ if and only if } P' = U,$$

respectively. The latter are easily proved theorems of our set algebra. [Cf. Lemma 1, Exercise 2 (page 69), and the corollary to Theorem 6, in Section 3 of Chapter 2.]

The "extended" De Morgan laws may be rendered in plain English as follows:

$$\sim[(\forall x \in U)\pi(x)] \Leftrightarrow (\exists x \in U)\tilde{\pi}(x):$$

Not every member of U satisfies condition π if and only if some member of U satisfies condition $\tilde{\pi}$.

$$\sim[(\exists x \in U)\pi(x)] \Leftrightarrow (\forall x \in U)\tilde{\pi}(x):$$

No member of U satisfies condition π if and only if every member of U satisfies condition $\tilde{\pi}$.

Compare (Section 1, Chapter 1) the question of negating *Each even number greater than 2 is the sum of two primes.*

EXERCISES

1. Give English versions for the negation of each sentence in the Exercises on page 91.

2. Suppose $U = \{a, b\}$. Write each of the following without quantifiers and show that it is a special case of some tautology of the algebra of statements:

$$(\exists x \in U)[\pi(x) \Rightarrow \rho(x)] \Leftrightarrow [(\forall x \in U)\pi(x) \Rightarrow (\exists x \in U)\rho(x)],$$
$$[(\exists x \in U)\pi(x) \Rightarrow (\forall x \in U)\rho(x)] \Rightarrow (\forall x \in U)[\pi(x) \Rightarrow \rho(x)],$$
$$[(\exists x \in U)\pi(x) \Rightarrow (\exists x \in U)\rho(x)] \Rightarrow (\exists x \in U)[\pi(x) \Rightarrow \rho(x)],$$
$$(\forall x \in U)[\pi(x) \Rightarrow \rho(x)] \Rightarrow [(\exists x \in U)\pi(x) \Rightarrow (\exists x \in U)\rho(x)].$$

3. Suppose $U = \{a, b, c\}$ and $S = \{a, b\}$. Write each of the following without quantifiers and show that it is a special case of a tautology in Chapter 1:

$$(\forall x \in U)\pi(x) \Rightarrow (\forall x \in S)\pi(x),$$
$$(\exists x \in S)\pi(x) \Rightarrow (\exists x \in U)\pi(x).$$

More Tautologies

Given any tautology from Chapter 1, for example, $p \wedge q \Rightarrow p$, we can certainly write any number of special cases involving some quantifiers. Thus

$$[(\forall x \in U)\pi(x)] \wedge [(\exists x \in U)\rho(x)] \Rightarrow (\forall x \in U)\pi(x)$$

is a tautology. The De Morgan tautologies, however, are not so trivial: if we analyze their structure by the methods of Chapter 1, we get $p \Leftrightarrow q$, or $\bar{p} \Leftrightarrow q$, neither of which is a tautology. We proved the De Morgan laws by translating them into theorems of set algebra. This trick works both ways. Consider, for example, property (ii): the transitivity of set inclusion,

$$\text{If } P \subseteq Q \text{ and } Q \subseteq R, \text{ then } P \subseteq R.$$

Writing

$$(\forall x \in U)[\pi(x) \Rightarrow \rho(x)] \qquad \text{for} \qquad P \subseteq Q,$$
$$(\forall x \in U)[\rho(x) \Rightarrow \sigma(x)] \qquad \text{for} \qquad Q \subseteq R,$$

and

$$(\forall x \in U)[\pi(x) \Rightarrow \sigma(x)] \qquad \text{for} \qquad P \subseteq R,$$

we get

$$(\forall x)[\pi(x) \Rightarrow \rho(x)] \wedge (\forall x)[\rho(x) \Rightarrow \sigma(x)] \Rightarrow (\forall x)[\pi(x) \Rightarrow \sigma(x)].$$

From this tautology and the De Morgan tautologies we can get the whole theory of "syllogisms," as we shall see in the next section.

We examine more examples of the method of translation and leave some others as exercises. In each example every quantifier refers to the same universe: to save space we suppress U, writing $(\forall x)$ and $(\exists x)$ for $(\forall x \in U)$ and $(\exists x \in U)$, respectively.

Example 1 $(\forall x)\pi(x) \Rightarrow (\forall x)[\pi(x) \vee \rho(x)]$.

Translation $(P = U) \Rightarrow (P \cup R = U)$.

Example 2 $(\forall x)[\pi(x) \wedge \rho(x)] \Rightarrow (\forall x)\pi(x)$.

Translation $(P \cap R = U) \Rightarrow (P = U)$.

Example 3 $(\forall x)\rho(x) \Rightarrow (\forall x)[\pi(x) \Rightarrow \rho(x)]$.

Translation $(R = U) \Rightarrow (P \subseteq R)$.

In each of these examples the translation is an easy theorem of set algebra:

1   If $P = U$, then $P \cup R = U \cup R$, but $U \cup R = U$, so $P \cup R = U$.
2   $P \cap R \subseteq P$, but if $P \cap R = U$, then $U \subseteq P$, so $P = U$.
3   Since $P \subseteq U$, $P \subseteq R$ if $R = U$.

In Examples 4, 5, 6 we go the other way:

Example 4 $P \subseteq P \cup R$.

Translation $(\forall x)\{\pi(x) \Rightarrow [\pi(x) \vee \rho(x)]\}$.

Example 5 $P \cap R \subseteq P$.

Translation $(\forall x)\{[\pi(x) \wedge \rho(x)] \Rightarrow \pi(x)\}$.

Example 6 $R \subseteq P' \cup R$

Translations $(\forall x)\{\rho(x) \Rightarrow [\bar{\pi}(x) \vee \rho(x)]\}$,

                          $(\forall x)\{\rho(x) \Rightarrow [\pi(x) \Rightarrow \rho(x)]\}$.

Later we shall examine other methods for obtaining tautologies. We shall find, for example, that the tautologies in the first three examples above may be deduced directly from those in the last three examples. (Cf. *change of scope*, Section 3.)

EXERCISE

1. Prove that the following are tautologies by translating them into set language and deducing the results as theorems of the algebra of sets:

$$(\forall x)[\pi(x) \Rightarrow \rho(x)] \Rightarrow (\forall x)[\pi(x) \Rightarrow \rho(x) \vee \sigma(x)],$$
$$(\forall x)[\pi(x) \Rightarrow \rho(x)] \Rightarrow (\forall x)[\pi(x) \wedge \sigma(x) \Rightarrow \rho(x)],$$
$$(\forall x)[\pi(x) \vee \rho(x) \Rightarrow \sigma(x)] \Rightarrow (\forall x)[\pi(x) \Rightarrow \sigma(x)],$$
$$(\forall x)[\pi(x) \Rightarrow \rho(x) \wedge \sigma(x)] \Rightarrow (\forall x)[\pi(x) \Rightarrow \rho(x)].$$

2. SYLLOGISMS AND SORITES

In Chapter 1 we saw that from the premises

> *All Greeks are men.*
> *All men are mortal.*

we could infer

> *All Greeks are Men.*

In this section we shall finally see that we can also infer

> *All Greeks are mortal.*

Our method for deriving conclusions from given premises is still just what it has been all along: we are obliged to find an appropriate tautology. The difference is simply that now we have more tautologies we can use.

In this section we examine two of the standard types of inferences of traditional logic: syllogisms and sorites (the latter are chains of syllogisms). In later sections we shall consider some other forms of inference.

It is easy to infer that Greeks are mortal, given the premises above. The relevant tautology is

$$(\forall x)[\pi(x) \Rightarrow \rho(x)] \wedge (\forall x)[\rho(x) \Rightarrow \sigma(x)] \Rightarrow (\forall x)[\pi(x) \Rightarrow \sigma(x)],$$

whose set version is just the assertion that inclusion is a transitive relation. (We may take for U the set of people.) An inference based on this tautology is the classic Aristotelean syllogism, known in traditional logic as BARBARA. Another classical syllogism, called DARII, is based on the tautology

$$(\forall x)[\pi(x) \Rightarrow \rho(x)] \wedge (\exists x)[\sigma(x) \wedge \pi(x)] \Rightarrow (\exists x)[\sigma(x) \wedge \rho(x)].$$

For example

> *All Greeks are men.*
> *Some soldiers are Greeks.*
> ∴ *Some soldiers are men.*

Another classic inference is this:

> *Socrates is Greek.*
> *All Greeks are mortal.*
> ∴ *Socrates is mortal.*

It is another example of BARBARA: replace $\pi(x)$, $\rho(x)$, $\sigma(x)$, respectively, by *x is Socrates, x is Greek*, and *x is mortal*.

There is a vast literature on syllogisms, beginning with the *Prior Analytics* of Aristotle (384–332 B.C.) and continuing to this day. One of the contributors to the subject is Lewis Carroll, whose book *Symbolic Logic* (1897) has many entertaining examples of syllogisms and sorites, some of which we shall examine. Carroll's problems are especially valuable for the practice they afford for symbolic analysis of "ordinary" English sentences.

A *syllogism* is an inference with two premises; each premise and the conclusion has one of the following four forms:

A: Each α is a β, $(\forall x)[\alpha(x) \Rightarrow \beta(x)]$,

I: Some α is a β, $(\exists x)[\alpha(x) \wedge \beta(x)]$,

E: No α is a β,   ' $(\forall x)[\alpha(x) \Rightarrow \tilde\beta(x)]$,

O: Some α is not a β, $(\exists x)[\alpha(x) \wedge \tilde\beta(x)]$.

The capital letters on the left (vowels in AFFIRMO and NEGO) are the traditional labels for these forms. Observe that O is the negation of A, and E the negation of I. Observe also that I and E are *symmetric*: interchanging α and β has no effect on either.

The three statements comprising a syllogism (the conclusion and the two premises) require three conditions, two of which appear in each statement. Of those in the conclusion, one appears in each premise; the third appears in both of the premises but not in the conclusion. Tradition demands that the letters S, M, P represent the conditions: S for the "first" and P for the "last" condition in the conclusion, and M for the "middle term" which appears only in the premises. If one demands that P be in the first premise, there are only four ways these three "terms" may be arranged:

I	II	III	IV
M P	P M	M P	P M
S M	S M	M S	M S
∴ S P	∴ S P	∴ S P	∴ S P

Each of these arrangements is called a *figure*; P is called the *major term* and S the *minor term*; the first premise is called the *major premise*, the second the *minor premise*. (The letters S and P were chosen because they are the initials of *subject* and *predicate*, respectively.)

The problem is to assign, to each premise and to the conclusion, one of the four letters A, I, E, O in such a way that the resulting inference pattern is valid. Of the 256 ($= 4 \cdot 4^3$) ways such assignments may be made, only 15 represent valid inferences. We list the results, using traditional "mnemonic" names:

I	II	III	IV
BARBARA	CESARE	DATISI	CALEMES
CELARENT	CAMESTRES	FERISO	FRESISON
DARII	FESTINO	DISAMIS	DIMATIS
FERIO	BAROCO	BOCARDO	

In these names the vowels indicate, in order, which of the four types of statement is used as major premise, minor premise, and conclusion. Thus BARBARA (first figure) is the inference

$$
\begin{array}{ll}
\text{M A P} & (\forall x)[\gamma(x) \implies \beta(x)], \\
\text{S A M} & (\forall x)[\alpha(x) \implies \gamma(x)], \\
\therefore \text{S A P} & \therefore (\forall x)[\alpha(x) \implies \beta(x)];
\end{array}
$$

BAROCO (second figure) is

$$
\begin{array}{ll}
\text{P A M} & (\forall x)[\beta(x) \implies \gamma(x)], \\
\text{S O M} & (\exists x)[\alpha(x) \wedge \tilde{\gamma}(x)], \\
\therefore \text{S O P} & \therefore (\exists x)[\alpha(x) \wedge \tilde{\beta}(x)];
\end{array}
$$

and FERISO (third figure) is

$$
\begin{array}{ll}
\text{M E P} & (\forall x)[\gamma(x) \implies \tilde{\beta}(x)], \\
\text{M I S} & (\exists x)[\gamma(x) \wedge \alpha(x)], \\
\therefore \text{S O P} & \therefore (\exists x)[\alpha(x) \wedge \tilde{\beta}(x)].
\end{array}
$$

In classical logic four more forms of syllogism were admitted, making a total of 19 "valid" forms. The others,

III	IV
*DARAPTI	*BAMALIP
*FELAPTON	*FESAPO,

were allowed under classical interpretations of A and E which, in our notation, amount to

$$
\begin{array}{ll}
\text{A*:} & (\exists x)\alpha(x) \wedge (\forall x)[\alpha(x) \implies \beta(x)], \\
\text{E*:} & (\exists x)\alpha(x) \wedge (\forall x)[\alpha(x) \implies \tilde{\beta}(x)].
\end{array}
$$

*BAMALIP is valid if some member of the relevant universe satisfies condition P; for the other three something must satisfy M. Let us consider such an "existential assumption" to be a "third premise," and retain the extra four forms for *auld lang syne*.

Here are some of Carroll's examples.

(1)   *Every eagle can fly.*
                     Some pigs cannot fly.

          ∴ *Some pigs are not eagles.*

This is an example of BAROCO (second figure): S for pigs, P for eagles, M for what can fly,

$$
\begin{array}{l}
\text{P A M} \\
\text{S O M} \qquad \text{(Universe: animals, e.g.).} \\
\therefore \text{S O P}
\end{array}
$$

(2)   *Gold is heavy.*
                Nothing but gold will silence him.
            ∴ *Nothing light will silence him.*

This is BARBARA (first figure): let S represent what will silence him, P what is heavy, and M what is gold. Thus

$$M\ A\ P$$
$$S\ \ A\ M \qquad \text{(Universe: things),}$$
$$∴ S\ \ A\ P$$

where the minor premise and the conclusion are written in contrapositive form.

(3)   *Your course is always honest.*
              Your course is always the best policy.
         ∴ *Honesty is sometimes the best policy.*

Let the universe be what one can do. Take S for what is honest, P for what is the best policy, and M for what you do (i.e., your course of action). The form is then *DARAPTI (third figure), with the premises interchanged:

$$M\ A\ P$$
$$M\ A\ S$$
$$∴ S\ \ I\ \ P.$$

The extra assumption is that you do something.

EXERCISES

Below are more of Carroll's examples of syllogisms. Classify each and, when necessary, state the existential assumption required:

1.   Some, who deserve the fair, get their deserts.
     None but the brave deserve the fair.
   ∴ Some brave persons get their deserts.

2.   Audible music causes vibrations in the air.
     Inaudible music is not worth paying for.
   ∴ No music is worth paying for, unless it causes vibrations in the air.

3.   Some holidays are rainy.
     Rainy days are tiresome.
   ∴ Some holidays are tiresome.

4.   No philosophers are conceited.
     Some conceited persons are not gamblers.
   ∴ Some people, who are not gamblers, are not philosophers.

5.   Nothing intelligible ever puzzles me.
     Logic puzzles me.
     ∴ Logic is unintelligible.

6.   No country, that has been explored, is infested by dragons.
     Unexplored countries are fascinating.
     ∴ No country infested by dragons fails to be fascinating.

7.   Some oysters are silent.
     No silent creatures are amusing.
     ∴ Some oysters are not amusing.

8.   All philosophers are logical.
     An illogical man is always obstinate.
     ∴ Some obstinate persons are not philosophers.

9.   No exciting books suit feverish patients.
     Unexciting books make one drowsy.
     ∴ No books suit feverish patients unless they make one drowsy.

10. When a man knows what he's about, he can detect a sharper.
     You and I know what we're about.
     ∴ You and I can detect a sharper.

11. Some dreams are terrible.
     No lambs are terrible.
     ∴ Some dreams are not lambs.

12. All clear explanations are satisfactory.
     Some excuses are unsatisfactory.
     ∴ Some excuses are not clear explanations.

13. None of my boys are clever.
     None of my girls are greedy.
     ∴ No clever child of mine is greedy.

14. All jokes are meant to amuse.
     No Act of Parliament is a joke.
     ∴ Some things, that are meant to amuse, are not Acts of Parliament.

Next we work one of Carroll's sorites problems, and leave a few more as exercises. Consider the following six premises:

(1) *Animals, that do not kick, are always unexcitable.*

(2) *Donkeys have no horns.*

(3) *A buffalo can always toss one over a gate.*

(4) *No animals that kick are easy to swallow.*

(5) *No hornless animals can toss one over a gate.*

(6) *All animals are excitable, except buffaloes.*

Take for universe the set of animals and introduce the following notation:

$\alpha(x)$: x *kicks*, $\beta(x)$: x *is excitable*,

$\gamma(x)$: x *is a donkey*, $\delta(x)$: x *has horns*,

$\epsilon(x)$: x *is a buffalo*, $\zeta(x)$: x *can toss one over a gate*,

$\eta(x)$: x *is easy to swallow*.

Then the premises are

(1) $(\forall x)[\tilde{\alpha}(x) \Rightarrow \tilde{\beta}(x)]$,   or $(\forall x)[\beta(x) \Rightarrow \alpha(x)]$,

(2) $(\forall x)[\gamma(x) \Rightarrow \tilde{\delta}(x)]$,

(3) $(\forall x)[\epsilon(x) \Rightarrow \zeta(x)]$,   or $(\forall x)[\tilde{\zeta}(x) \Rightarrow \tilde{\epsilon}(x)]$,

(4) $\sim(\exists x)[\alpha(x) \wedge \eta(x)]$,   i.e. $(\forall x)[\alpha(x) \Rightarrow \tilde{\eta}(x)]$,

(5) $\sim(\exists x)[\tilde{\delta}(x) \wedge \zeta(x)]$,   i.e. $(\forall x)[\tilde{\delta}(x) \Rightarrow \tilde{\zeta}(x)]$,

(6) $(\forall x)[\tilde{\epsilon}(x) \Rightarrow \beta(x)]$.

We combine premises as follows:

(7) $(\forall x)[\gamma(x) \Rightarrow \tilde{\zeta}(x)]$,   [(2) and (5)

(8) $(\forall x)[\gamma(x) \Rightarrow \tilde{\epsilon}(x)]$,   [(7) and (3)

(9) $(\forall x)[\gamma(x) \Rightarrow \beta(x)]$,   [(8) and (6)

(10) $(\forall x)[\gamma(x) \Rightarrow \alpha(x)]$,   [(9) and (1)

(11) $(\forall x)[\gamma(x) \Rightarrow \tilde{\eta}(x)]$.   [(10) and (4)

Conclusion: *Donkeys are not easy to swallow.*

EXERCISES

Carroll gives the following sets of premises: you are to draw a conclusion.

1. No terriers wander among the signs of the zodiac. Nothing, that does not wander among the signs of the zodiac, is a comet. Nothing but a terrier has a curly tail.

2. All members of the House of Commons have perfect self-command. No M.P., who wears a coronet, should ride in a donkey-race. All members of the House of Lords wear coronets.

3. Things sold in the street are of no great value. Nothing but rubbish can be had for a song. Eggs of the Great Auk are very valuable. It is only what is sold in the street that is really rubbish.

4. No kitten, that loves fish, is unteachable. No kitten without a tail will play with a gorilla. Kittens with whiskers always love fish. No teachable kitten has green eyes. No kittens have tails unless they have whiskers.

5. No shark ever doubts that it is well fitted out. A fish, that cannot dance a minuet, is contemptible. No fish is quite certain that it is well fitted out, unless

it has three rows of teeth. All fishes, except sharks, are kind to children. No heavy fish can dance a minuet. A fish with three rows of teeth is not to be despised.

6. The only animals in this house are cats. Every animal is suitable for a pet, that loves to gaze at the moon. When I detest an animal, I avoid it. No animals are carnivorous, unless they prowl at night. No cat fails to kill mice. No animals ever take to me, except what are in this house. Kangaroos are not suitable for pets. None but carnivora kill mice. I detest animals that do not take to me. Animals, that prowl at night, always love to gaze at the moon.

Carroll's answers:

1. No comet has a curly tail.

2. No M.P. should ride in a donkey race, unless he has perfect self-command.

3. An egg of the Great Auk is not to be had for a song.

4. No kitten with green eyes will play with a gorilla.

5. No heavy fish is unkind to children.

6. I always avoid a kangaroo.

Derivation of The Valid Forms

Three simple ideas suffice to justify all fifteen syllogisms, given that any one of them is valid. They are these:

(1) Contraposition (cf. Section 6, Chapter 1), using that fact that A and O are negations of one another, as are I and E.

(2) "Conversion," based on the symmetry of I and E.

(3) Replacing β by $\tilde{\beta}$ interchanges A and E, as well as I and O.

Let us begin with BARBARA which is based on the tautology

$$(\forall x)[\rho(x) \Rightarrow \sigma(x)] \wedge (\forall x)[\pi(x) \Rightarrow \rho(x)] \Rightarrow (\forall x)[\pi(x) \Rightarrow \sigma(x)],$$

whose set version is the transitivity of inclusion [property (ii)]. Contraposition transforms BARBARA into BAROCO and BOCARDO.

Putting $\tilde{P}$ for P, BARBARA is transformed into CELARENT, and contraposition transforms CELARENT into DISAMIS and FESTINO.

Conversion (of premises) yields the following transformations.

CELARENT ↔ CESARE,	CAMESTRES ↔ CALEMES,	
DARII ↔ DATISI,	DISAMIS ↔ DIMATIS,	
FERIO ↔ FESTINO ↔ FERISO ↔ FRESISON.		

Finally, interchanging S and P (conversion of the conclusion) and the order of premises gives

CESARE ↔ CAMESTRES,

DATISI ↔ DISAMIS;

and we are done.

EXERCISES

1. Verify the transformations just described.
2. Transform the four "extra" syllogisms, using the same techniques, and explain why the five other forms you get are not worth adding to the traditional nineteen.
3. Establish the validity of the "starred" forms (those requiring existential assumptions).

3. MORE TAUTOLOGIES

In this section we examine some more tautologies (which will prove very useful later) and we discuss another method for deriving tautologies.

Deduction of Tautologies

In Chapter 1 we considered two ways to get tautologies: from truth tables, and by "algebraic derivation" from the basic laws. There is a third method we might have used, but did not for two reasons: we concentrated on equivalences and derivation techniques so that we could exploit similarities between elementary algebra and statement algebra, and also so that we could emphasize the analogy between statement algebra and the set algebra of Chapter 2.

The third way to get tautologies uses the process of inference and is important because, of the three, only it works just as well for tautologies with quantifiers as for the tautologies of Chapter 1. The idea is quite simple: if the premises of an inference are tautologies, the conclusion must be a tautology too.

Example 1 (*Algebra of Statements*) Given the tautology

$$(p \Rightarrow q) \Rightarrow (p \Rightarrow q)$$

(a special case of $p \Rightarrow p$) as premise, and the tautology

$$[q \Rightarrow (p \Rightarrow r)] \Rightarrow (p \wedge q \Rightarrow r)$$

to justify the inference, we may deduce T-4:

$$p \wedge (p \Rightarrow q) \Rightarrow q.$$

Here the premise, being a tautology, can have no false "instances"; hence the conclusion can have none either, so it also is a tautology.

Example 2 (*De Morgan*) Given

$$\sim[(\forall x \in U)\pi(x)] \Leftrightarrow (\exists x \in U)\bar{\pi}(x)$$

as premise, and

$$(p \Leftrightarrow q) \Leftrightarrow (\bar{q} \Leftrightarrow \bar{p})$$

as the tautology to justify the inference, we conclude that

$$\sim[(\exists x \in U)\bar{\pi}(x)] \Leftrightarrow (\forall x \in U)\pi(x)$$

is a tautology. Putting $\bar{\pi}$ for π, we obtain

$$\sim[(\exists x \in U)\pi(x)] \Leftrightarrow (\forall x \in U)\bar{\pi}(x)$$

as a special case; so it is a tautology also. Thus one of the extended De Morgan tautologies is a consequence of the other. Indeed each of them is a consequence of the other—in the language of Chapter 1, they are transformations of each other.

In each of these examples the tautology invoked to justify the inference is one from the algebra of statements ($[q \Rightarrow (p \Rightarrow r)] \Rightarrow (p \wedge q \Rightarrow r)$ and $(p \Leftrightarrow q) \Leftrightarrow (\bar{q} \Leftrightarrow \bar{p})$, respectively). We shall encounter other examples in which the inferences are based on tautologies with quantifiers. (Example 4, below, is one.)

Change of Scope

We now consider some tautologies of a type which will prove to be very useful in a variety of problems: they permit us to combine—or to break down—quantified open sentences, and are somewhat analogous to factorization rules of elementary algebra.

Example 3

$$(\forall x)[\pi(x) \wedge \rho(x)] \Leftrightarrow [(\forall x)\pi(x)] \wedge [(\forall x)\rho(x)].$$

Translating, we have

$$(P \cap R = U) \Leftrightarrow (P = U) \wedge (R = U).$$

The *if* part ($\Leftarrow$) follows from the idempotence of intersection [Theorem 4(1), Section 3, Chapter 2]. For the *only if* part ($\Rightarrow$) suppose $P \cap R = U$. Since $P \cap R \subseteq P \subseteq U$, it follows that $U \subseteq P \subseteq U$ and $P = U$. Similarly, $U = P \cap R \subseteq R \subseteq U$ gives $R = U$.

We can describe this tautology, a bit picturesquely perhaps, by saying that a universal quantifier "distributes over" a conjunction. The next example is the analogue for existential quantifiers and disjunction. If the universe is finite, for example if it has 2, or 3, or 700 members, these tautologies can be proved using the commutativity and associativity of conjunction and disjunction, respectively. Thus, if $U = \{a, b\}$, Example 3 boils down to

$$[\pi(a) \wedge \rho(a)] \wedge [\pi(b) \wedge \rho(b)] \Leftrightarrow [\pi(a) \wedge \pi(b)] \wedge [\rho(a) \wedge \rho(b)].$$

Example 4

$$(\exists x)[\pi(x) \vee \rho(x)] \Leftrightarrow [(\exists x)\pi(x)] \vee [(\exists x)\rho(x)].$$

Using De Morgan laws, we see that this is essentially the contrapositive of the tautology in Example 3: negating each side gives

$$(\forall x)[\bar{\pi}(x) \wedge \bar{\rho}(x)] \Leftrightarrow [(\forall x)\bar{\pi}(x)] \wedge [(\forall x)\bar{\rho}(x)].$$

Another version of Example 4 is left as an exercise (1-A3, below).

The change-of-scope tautologies mentioned so far are two-way implications. Some others are not.

Example 5

$$(\exists x)[\pi(x) \wedge \rho(x)] \Rightarrow [(\exists x)\pi(x)] \wedge [(\exists x)\rho(x)].$$

Translating, we have

$$(P \cap R \neq \varnothing) \Rightarrow (P \neq \varnothing) \wedge (R \neq \varnothing)$$

or, taking the contrapositive, we get

$$(P = \varnothing) \vee (R = \varnothing) \Rightarrow (P \cap R = \varnothing).$$

Proof. $\varnothing \subseteq P \cap R \subseteq P = \varnothing$, so $P \cap R = \varnothing$; similarly, $P \cap R = \varnothing$ if $R = \varnothing$. The converse, however, cannot be proved in general; in fact, for arbitrary π, ρ, it holds if and only if U is void or a singleton. Suppose, for example, that $U = \{a, b\}$. Then

$$(\exists x)[\pi(x) \wedge \rho(x)] \Leftrightarrow [\pi(a) \wedge \rho(a)] \vee [\pi(b) \wedge \rho(b)]$$
$$\Leftrightarrow [\pi(a) \vee \pi(b)] \wedge [\pi(a) \vee \rho(b)]$$
$$\wedge [\rho(a) \vee \pi(b)] \wedge [\rho(a) \vee \rho(b)],$$

but

$$[(\exists x)\pi(x)] \wedge [(\exists x)\rho(x)] \Leftrightarrow [\pi(a) \vee \pi(b)] \wedge [\rho(a) \vee \rho(b)].$$

If $U = \varnothing$, the corresponding expressions are both false and if U is a singleton $\{a\}$, each is just $\pi(a) \wedge \rho(a)$. But if U has two or more members, it has a nonvoid subset whose complement is nonvoid and such a pair of subsets provides a counterexample for the converse: $P = \varnothing$ or $R = \varnothing$ if $P \cap R = \varnothing$.

Two more versions of the tautology in Example 5 are left as exercises (B1 and B3, below), along with several other change-of-scope tautologies.

EXERCISE

1. Complete the project, begun above, of proving each of the following change-of-scope tautologies:

　A1.　$(\forall x)[\pi(x) \wedge \rho(x)] \Leftrightarrow (\forall x)\pi(x) \wedge (\forall x)\rho(x)$

　A2.　$(\exists x)[\pi(x) \vee \rho(x)] \Leftrightarrow (\exists x)\pi(x) \vee (\exists x)\rho(x)$

　A3.　$(\exists x)[\pi(x) \Rightarrow \rho(x)] \Leftrightarrow [(\forall x)\pi(x) \Rightarrow (\exists x)\rho(x)]$

B1. $(\forall x)\pi(x) \lor (\forall x)\rho(x) \Rightarrow (\forall x)[\pi(x) \lor \rho(x)]$

B2. $(\exists x)[\pi(x) \land \rho(x)] \Rightarrow (\exists x)\pi(x) \land (\exists x)\rho(x)$

B3. $[(\exists x)\pi(x) \Rightarrow (\forall x)\rho(x)] \Rightarrow (\forall x)[\pi(x) \Rightarrow \rho(x)]$

C1. $(\forall x)[\pi(x) \Rightarrow \rho(x)] \Rightarrow [(\forall x)\pi(x) \Rightarrow (\forall x)\rho(x)]$

C2.* $[(\exists x)\pi(x) \Rightarrow (\exists x)\rho(x)] \Rightarrow (\exists x)[\pi(x) \Rightarrow \rho(x)]$

D1. $(\forall x)[\pi(x) \lor \rho(x)] \Rightarrow [(\forall x)\pi(x) \lor (\exists x)\rho(x)]$

D2. $[(\exists x)\pi(x) \land (\forall x)\rho(x)] \Rightarrow (\exists x)[\pi(x) \land \rho(x)]$

D3. $(\forall x)[\pi(x) \Rightarrow \rho(x)] \Rightarrow [(\exists x)\pi(x) \Rightarrow (\exists x)\rho(x)]$

E1. $(\forall x)[\pi(x) \Leftrightarrow \rho(x)] \Rightarrow [(\forall x)\pi(x) \Leftrightarrow (\forall x)\rho(x)]$

E2. $(\forall x)[\pi(x) \Leftrightarrow \rho(x)] \Rightarrow [(\exists x)\pi(x) \Leftrightarrow (\exists x)\rho(x)]$

Each tautological implication of statement algebra has an analogue in our condition algebra. For example,

$$\pi \Rightarrow \pi \lor \rho \equiv I,$$
$$\pi \land (\pi \Rightarrow \rho) \Rightarrow \rho \equiv I,$$

etc. But, then

$$(\forall x \in U)[\pi(x) \Rightarrow \pi(x) \lor \rho(x)],$$
$$(\forall x \in U)\{\pi(x) \land [\pi(x) \Rightarrow \rho(x)] \Rightarrow \rho(x)\},$$

etc., are tautologies. Using change-of-scope tautologies to justify the inferences, we may deduce others from these. For example, C1 gives

$$(\forall x \in U)\pi(x) \Rightarrow (\forall x \in U)[\pi(x) \lor \rho(x)],$$
$$(\forall x \in U)\{\pi(x) \land [\pi(x) \Rightarrow \rho(x)]\} \Rightarrow (\forall x \in U)\rho(x),$$

etc., and D3 gives

$$(\exists x \in U)\pi(x) \Rightarrow (\exists x \in U)[\pi(x) \lor \rho(x)],$$
$$(\exists x \in U)\{\pi(x) \land [\pi(x) \Rightarrow \rho(x)]\} \Rightarrow (\exists x \in U)\rho(x),$$

etc. And, using A1 in the hypothesis of

$$(\forall x)\{\pi(x) \land [\pi(x) \Rightarrow \rho(x)]\} \Rightarrow (\forall x)\rho(x),$$

we can get

$$(\forall x)\pi(x) \land (\forall x)[\pi(x) \Rightarrow \rho(x)] \Rightarrow (\forall x)\rho(x).$$

These techniques permit us to "carry over" a great many tautologies from Chapter 1, some of which we have already obtained by other methods. Each of the basic laws and all the other equivalences of Chapter 1 yield at

---

* C2 requires a special assumption: $U \neq \varnothing$.

least a pair of "two-way tautologies": for example,

$$(\forall x)[\pi(x) \wedge \rho(x)] \Leftrightarrow (\forall x)[\rho(x) \wedge \pi(x)],$$
$$(\exists x)[\pi(x) \wedge \rho(x)] \Leftrightarrow (\exists x)[\rho(x) \wedge \pi(x)];$$
$$(\forall x)[\pi(x) \Rightarrow \rho(x)] \Leftrightarrow (\forall x)[\bar{\rho}(x) \Rightarrow \bar{\pi}(x)],$$
$$(\exists x)[\pi(x) \Rightarrow \rho(x)] \Leftrightarrow (\exists x)[\bar{\rho}(x) \Rightarrow \bar{\pi}(x)];$$

etc.

EXERCISES

1. Write out all the tautologies you can get from T-1, ..., T-11, page 25, using the method described above.

2. Justify the following tautologies:

$$(\forall x)[\pi(x) \Rightarrow \rho(x)] \Rightarrow (\forall x)[\pi(x) \wedge \sigma(x) \Rightarrow \rho(x) \wedge \sigma(x)],$$
$$(\forall x)[\pi(x) \Rightarrow \rho(x)] \Rightarrow (\forall x)[\pi(x) \vee \sigma(x) \Rightarrow \rho(x) \vee \sigma(x)],$$
$$(\forall x)\{\pi(x) \Rightarrow [\rho(x) \Rightarrow \sigma(x)]\} \Leftrightarrow (\forall x)[\pi(x) \wedge \rho(x) \Rightarrow \sigma(x)],$$
$$(\forall x)[\pi(x) \Rightarrow \rho(x)] \wedge (\forall x)[\pi(x) \Rightarrow \sigma(x)] \Leftrightarrow (\forall x)[\pi(x) \Rightarrow \rho(x) \wedge \sigma(x)],$$
$$(\exists x)[\pi(x) \Rightarrow \rho(x)] \vee (\exists x)[\pi(x) \Rightarrow \sigma(x)] \Leftrightarrow (\exists x)[\pi(x) \Rightarrow \rho(x) \vee \sigma(x)].$$

Restricting and Extending Quantifiers

In Section 1 we parsed *All men are mortal* in two ways:

$$(\forall x \in U)\beta(x) \quad \text{and} \quad (\forall x \in V)[\alpha(x) \Rightarrow \beta(x)],$$

with U the set of men, V the set of people, $\alpha(x)$ for x *is a man* and $\beta(x)$ for x *is mortal*. Here we consider how "restricting" a quantifier to a subset of its universe can account for this difference.

Suppose, indeed, that α is a condition on U and that S is a subset of U. We wish to compare quantifiers "on U" with quantifiers "on S." If A is the extension of α in U, then a member of S satisfies α if and only if it is also a member of A: the extension of α "in S" is $A \cap S$. Thus, in particular, every member of S satisfies α if every member of U does, and some member of U does if some member of S does, and we have the tautologies: for $S \subseteq U$,

$$(\forall x \in U)\pi(x) \Rightarrow (\forall x \in S)\pi(x),$$
$$(\exists x \in S)\pi(x) \Rightarrow (\exists x \in U)\pi(x).$$

In view of the extended De Morgan tautologies, these two are essentially contrapositives of each other. Their translations in set language are

$$P \cap S = S \quad \text{if} \quad P = U,$$
$$P \neq \emptyset \quad \text{if} \quad P \cap S \neq \emptyset,$$

respectively.

For example, the commutative law for addition of real numbers can be expressed by the open sentence

$$x + y = y + x,$$

quantified over all pairs (x, y) of real numbers. "Restricting" the quantifier to the subset of all pairs (x, y) of rational numbers yields the commutative law for addition of rational numbers as an immediate consequence.

As the example just given should indicate, these tautologies are quite useful—a fact we shall confirm as we proceed. We call them *subalternations*.

One particular case is especially interesting. Suppose U is not void and that S is a singleton, say $S = \{a\}$. Then

$$(\forall x \in S)\pi(x) \Leftrightarrow \pi(a),$$
$$(\exists x \in S)\pi(x) \Leftrightarrow \pi(a),$$

so our tautologies can be written

$$(\forall x \in U)\pi(x) \Rightarrow \pi(a),$$
$$\pi(a) \Rightarrow (\exists x \in U)\pi(x);$$

and, from them, we may infer

$$(\forall x \in U)\pi(x) \Rightarrow (\exists x \in U)\pi(x).$$

Note that the last is no tautology if $U = \emptyset$; note also that its derivation breaks down just in this case.

The subalternation tautologies can be improved. As they stand they are one-way implications. If we introduce a condition whose extension in U is S, we can get two-way implications. Suppose $S = (\text{Ext } \sigma) \subseteq U$. Then

$$(\forall x \in S)\pi(x) \Leftrightarrow (\forall x \in U)[\sigma(x) \Rightarrow \pi(x)],$$
$$(\exists x \in S)\pi(x) \Leftrightarrow (\exists x \in U)[\sigma(x) \land \pi(x)]$$

are tautologies. Indeed, because $S \cap P$ is the extension of π in S if P is its extension in U, the set translation of the first is

$$S \cap P = S \qquad \text{if and only if} \qquad S \subseteq P.$$

The second (whose set version is fascinatingly trivial) is essentially the contrapositive of the first since

$$[\sim(\forall x \in S)\pi(x)] \Leftrightarrow (\exists x \in S)\bar{\pi}(x)$$

and

$$\{\sim(\forall x \in U)[\sigma(x) \Rightarrow \pi(x)]\} \Leftrightarrow (\exists x \in U)[\sigma(x) \land \bar{\pi}(x)].$$

We apply these results to a discussion of the relation between the following pair of tautologies:

I. $(\forall x \in U)[\pi(x) \Rightarrow \rho(x)] \land (\forall x \in U)[\rho(x) \Rightarrow \sigma(x)]$
$$\Rightarrow (\forall x \in U)[\pi(x) \Rightarrow \sigma(x)],$$

II. $(\forall x \in U)\rho(x) \wedge (\forall x \in U)[\rho(x) \Rightarrow \sigma(x)] \Rightarrow (\forall x \in U)\sigma(x).$

Here I is the tautology justifying BARBARA; II is a special case of I which can be obtained merely by restricting π to be a condition whose extension is U. Indeed, if π has extension U, then (by the first of our two-way sub-alternations)

$$(\forall x \in U)[\pi(x) \Rightarrow \rho(x)] \Leftrightarrow (\forall x \in U)\rho(x)$$

and

$$(\forall x \in U)[\pi(x) \Rightarrow \sigma(x)] \Leftrightarrow (\forall x \in U)\sigma(x).$$

So, for this case, I reduces to II. But, as a matter of fact, the special case II has the same force as the more "general" form I: that is, I can also be derived from II.

To derive I, we assume the hypothesis

$$(\forall x \in U)[\pi(x) \Rightarrow \rho(x)] \wedge (\forall x \in U)[\rho(x) \Rightarrow \sigma(x)].$$

We are to deduce $(\forall x \in U)[\pi(x) \Rightarrow \sigma(x)]$. Now

$$(\forall x \in U)[\pi(x) \Rightarrow \rho(x)] \Leftrightarrow (\forall x \in P)\rho(x),$$
$$(\forall x \in U)[\rho(x) \Rightarrow \sigma(x)] \Rightarrow (\forall x \in P)[\rho(x) \Rightarrow \sigma(x)],$$

by our subalternation tautologies, if $P = (\text{Ext } \pi) \subseteq U$. Our original premise thus yields

$$(\forall x \in P)\rho(x) \wedge (\forall x \in P)[\rho(x) \Rightarrow \sigma(x)],$$

from which we may infer $(\forall x \in P)\sigma(x)$ using II with P as universe. But, again,

$$(\forall x \in P)\sigma(x) \Leftrightarrow (\forall x \in U)[\pi(x) \Rightarrow \sigma(x)]$$

since $P = \text{Ext } \pi$; and we are done.

A third useful tautology, related to I and II, is

III. $\rho(a) \wedge (\forall x \in U)[\rho(x) \Rightarrow \sigma(x)] \Rightarrow \sigma(a),$ if $a \in U.$

Tautology III is surely the most natural tautology to invoke in the inference, mentioned in Section 2, for the mortality of Socrates. III is easy, for, with $a \in U$,

$$(\forall x \in U)[\rho(x) \Rightarrow \sigma(x)] \Rightarrow [\rho(a) \Rightarrow \sigma(a)],$$

restricting the quantifier on U to the subset $\{a\}$. Thus

$$\rho(a) \wedge (\forall x \in U)[\rho(x) \Rightarrow \sigma(x)] \Rightarrow \rho(a) \wedge [\rho(a) \Rightarrow \sigma(a)].$$

However,

$$\rho(a) \wedge [\rho(a) \Rightarrow \sigma(a)] \Rightarrow \sigma(a)$$

[an instance of the tautology $p \wedge (p \Rightarrow q) \Rightarrow q$ from Chapter 1], so III follows if we invoke $(p \Rightarrow q) \wedge (q \Rightarrow r) \Rightarrow (p \Rightarrow r)$.

EXERCISES

1. Using change-of-scope tautologies B1 and B2, deduce

$$(\exists x \in S)\pi(x) \Rightarrow (\exists x \in U)\pi(x)$$

and

$$(\forall x \in U)\pi(x) \Rightarrow (\forall x \in S)\pi(x)$$

from

$$(\exists x \in S)\pi(x) \Leftrightarrow (\exists x \in U)[\sigma(x) \wedge \pi(x)]$$

and

$$(\forall x \in S)\pi(x) \Leftrightarrow (\forall x \in U)[\sigma(x) \Rightarrow \pi(x)],$$

respectively.

2. Use change-of-scope tautology A3 to show that

$$(\forall x \in U)\pi(x) \Rightarrow (\exists x \in U)\pi(x)$$

is a tautology if and only if $U \neq \emptyset$.

Degenerate Conditions

Often it is convenient, appropriate, or necessary, to parse statements in a "mixed" form, combining conditions and quantifiers (as in Section 1) with statements which are not analyzed (as in Chapter 1). For example,

Either the sun is shining, or someone is lying:

$$a \vee (\exists x)\beta(x).$$

If all politicians are crooks, the country has had it:

$$(\forall x)\alpha(x) \Rightarrow b.$$

If something happens, you lose:

$$(\exists x)\alpha(x) \Rightarrow b.$$

You lose no matter what happens:

$$(\forall x)[\alpha(x) \Rightarrow b].$$

The statements treated in these examples as atomic could, of course, be analyzed further, but—for this discussion—there is no point in doing so. The essential thing is that a variable, x, appears on only one side of a connective ($\vee$, $\Rightarrow$ in these examples), not on both sides as in the change-of-scope tautologies. In Sections 4 and 5 we shall encounter open sentences with more than just a single variable: there we shall often find some variables isolated in this fashion, while others are not. (In *All hope abandon, ye who enter*, *hope* is isolated, *ye* is not.) The question at issue now is a special case of that more general problem. Our solution for the simpler problem will be carried over to the more general case when we get to it.

We use a conceptual trick. We imagine that a statement expresses a degenerate kind of condition: one which is either true for every member of U or is false for every member of U. Some writers refer to conditions as *propositional functions*, using the noun in the mathematical sense: U is the "domain" of the function and {T, F} is its "range," for to each member of U the condition assigns T or F according as the member belongs or does not belong to the extension of the condition. From this point of view, our "degenerate conditions" are just "constant functions": either T is assigned to every member of U or F is. In the terminology of "advanced" calculus, such a function is *independent of x*.

Thus we define a condition to be *degenerate*, or *constant*, on U if its extension in U is either $\emptyset$ or U. Observe, in particular, that if U itself is either void or a singleton, every condition on U is degenerate; in this case the only subsets of U are $\emptyset$ and U. If U is neither void nor a singleton it contains so-called *proper* subsets: nonvoid subsets whose complements are nonvoid. No condition whose extension is a proper subset of the universe is degenerate on that universe. However, every condition is degenerate on at least one subset (for example, its extension) which may or may not be void.

Suppose α is a condition degenerate on U. Then the open sentence $\alpha(x)$ is either true for each member of U, or it is false for each member of U. So, unless $U = \emptyset$, the statements $(\forall x \in U)\alpha(x)$ and $(\exists x \in U)\alpha(x)$ have the same truth value; indeed the same truth value as $\alpha(a)$ if a is any member of U. Hence, if $U \neq \emptyset$, and if we are given a degenerate condition, we may insert, remove, or switch quantifiers at will.

For example, we can rewrite our versions of the last two statements parsed above as follows:

$$(\exists x)\alpha(x) \Rightarrow (\forall x)\beta(x) \quad \text{for} \quad (\exists x)\alpha(x) \Rightarrow b,$$
$$(\forall x)[\alpha(x) \Rightarrow \beta(x)] \quad \text{for} \quad (\forall x)[\alpha(x) \Rightarrow b].$$

Here, if $U \neq \emptyset$, we take β to be a degenerate condition whose extension is U in case b is true, and $\emptyset$ if b is false. Thus, in either case, if $a \in U$, $\beta(a)$ and b have the same truth-value. In the first of these revisions we put $(\forall x)\beta(x)$ in place of b. In the second we consider $\alpha \Rightarrow \beta$ and $\alpha \Rightarrow b$ equivalent conditions; then the two quantified versions have the same truth-value. (Observe that even if U *is* void, the original and the revised versions of each of the statements have the same truth values.)

There is a point to these shenanigans. Now we can prove that the original statements "say the same thing"! One of our change-of-scope tautologies (B3) is

$$[(\exists x)\pi(x) \Rightarrow (\forall x)\rho(x)] \Rightarrow (\forall x)[\pi(x) \Rightarrow \rho(x)];$$

so *You lose no matter what happens* is a consequence of *If something happens, you lose.* But, in fact, the converse of B3 is a "tautology" if we add the proviso that ρ be degenerate on U. Suppose indeed that ρ is degenerate on U: $(R \neq U) \Rightarrow (R = \emptyset)$. To show

$$(P \subseteq R) \Rightarrow [(P \neq \emptyset) \Rightarrow (R = U)]$$

or

$$(P \subseteq R) \wedge (R \neq U) \Rightarrow (P = \emptyset).$$

If $P \subseteq R$ but $R \neq U$, then $P \subseteq R$ and $R = \emptyset$; so $P = \emptyset$. Q.E.D.

By adding suitable provisos restricting the kind of conditions which may replace π, ρ in our change-of-scope tautologies, we can prove the converse of each of those which, in general, goes only one-way. We announce the results, and leave the proofs as an exercise:

> For group B: At least one of π, ρ degenerate.
> For group C: π degenerate.
> For group D: ρ degenerate.
> For group E: Both π and ρ degenerate.

(Because every condition is degenerate on U if U is either void or a singleton, all these requirements are satisfied automatically if U is "small enough.")

We may express our results on the quantification of degenerate conditions by saying that for $U \neq \emptyset$,

$$p \Leftrightarrow (\forall x \in U)p \qquad \text{and} \qquad (\exists x \in U)p \Leftrightarrow p$$

are tautologies. Here p is a statement symbol, interpreted as a condition degenerate on U.

But, even if $U = \emptyset$, we can say that

$$p \Rightarrow (\forall x \in U)p \qquad \text{and} \qquad (\exists x \in U)p \Rightarrow p$$

are tautologies. So, in an inference problem (even if we do not know that $U \neq \emptyset$), we can at least add a universal quantifier, or drop an existential quantifier, *if* its scope is degenerate. Consider the possibilities: p can be assigned truth values T or F and U is either void or not.

$(\forall x \in U)p$				$(\exists x \in U)p$		
	$U = \emptyset$	$U \neq \emptyset$			$U = \emptyset$	$U \neq \emptyset$
p: T	T	T		p: T	F	T
F	T	F		F	F	F

These tables exhibit the truth values of the quantified forms for each of the four possibilities. The first shows that $(\forall x)p$ is true if p is; and the second shows that p is true if $(\exists x)p$ is. We shall have occasion to apply these tautologies in Section 5 when we consider problems of inference involving products.

EXERCISE

1. Obtain the following tautologies from those in Exercise 1 on page 105. Here p and r are statement symbols to be interpreted as representing degenerate conditions.

$$(\forall x)[p \lor \rho(x)] \Leftrightarrow p \lor (\forall x)\rho(x)$$
$$(\exists x)[p \land \rho(x)] \Leftrightarrow p \land (\exists x)\rho(x)$$

$$(\forall x)[p \Rightarrow \rho(x)] \Leftrightarrow [p \Rightarrow (\forall x)\rho(x)]$$
$$(\exists x)[p \Rightarrow \rho(x)] \Leftrightarrow [p \Rightarrow (\exists x)\rho(x)]$$

$$(\forall x)[\pi(x) \Rightarrow r] \Leftrightarrow \{[(\exists x)\pi(x)] \Rightarrow r\}$$
$$(\exists x)[\pi(x) \Rightarrow r] \Leftrightarrow \{[(\forall x)\pi(x)] \Rightarrow r\}$$

(For the fourth and sixth, $U \neq \emptyset$ is required for $\Leftarrow$.)

4. PRODUCTS, RELATIONS, AND MULTIPLE QUANTIFICATION

René Descartes, who published the first book on the subject in 1637, usually gets the credit for inventing analytic geometry. This feat was accomplished by means of the following inspiration. Imagine a plane containing a pair of "number lines" laid at right angles (see figure). Each point P in the plane determines a unique "ordered pair" (x, y) of real numbers: x is the number associated with the foot of the perpendicular from P to the "first" line, and y that associated with the foot of the perpendicular from P to the "second."

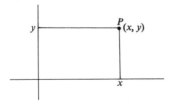

Moreover, any given "ordered pair" (x, y) of real numbers determines a unique point in the plane which may be constructed by erecting perpendiculars to the appropriate reference lines at the points associated with x and y. This idea of Descartes is that underlying the drawing of graphs—using geometrical figures to represent numerical relationships. Its historical significance stems in large part from the fact that it revolutionized geometry by opening the door for the use of algebraic techniques in the solution of geometrical problems: geometrical questions about points, and collections of points, can be translated into questions about ordered pairs of numbers and collections of the latter. In the three-and-a-quarter centuries since Descartes introduced his idea, it has been put to a variety of uses, many of which have little or no connection with geometrical questions. In this section, we adapt Descartes' idea to the study of some of the problems grammarians classify under the titles "direct objects" and "indirect objects."

Suppose we are given two nonvoid sets A and B, which may be equal but need not be. (In Descartes' case, they are equal: each is the set of real numbers.) We are interested in "ordered pairs" (a, b) with first component a member of A, second a member of B. More than this; we are interested in the set of all "ordered pairs" (a, b) where $a \in A$, $b \in B$. To say that a "pair" is "ordered" is to say that it makes a difference which component is first and which is second. This distinction is expressed by the criterion we adopt for equality of ordered pairs:

$$(a, b) = (c, d) \quad \text{if and only if} \quad a = c \quad \text{and} \quad b = d.$$

We shall refer to the set of all ordered pairs (a, b) where $a \in A$ and $b \in B$ as the *cartesian product* of the sets A, B and denote it by $A \times B$. (If either A or B is void, we take $A \times B$ to be void too.)

We may also consider "ordered triples," "ordered quadruples," etc.,

$$(a, b, c), \quad (a, b, c, d), \quad (a, b, c, d, e), \quad \ldots,$$

where $a \in A$, $b \in B$, $c \in C$, $d \in D$, $e \in E$, etc., and study the "products"

$$A \times B \times C, \quad A \times B \times C \times D, \quad A \times B \times C \times D \times E, \quad \ldots$$

consisting of all such triples, quadruples, etc.

There are a number of delicate problems related to the question of our right to discuss "ordered couples," "ordered triples," ..., and "cartesian products" of sets. As we have seen, in connection with Russell's paradox, we court disaster if we discuss "new" sets simply because we want to, or because we think they might be interesting or useful, no matter how carefully we may undertake to describe them. For all we can say at this point, the mere assumption that couples and products "exist" may very well lead to such an impasse as that obtained when we assumed there was a set among whose members every set could be found. We leave for an appendix a discussion of attempts to rationalize the difficulties involved. For the present, we undertake the project of showing that products are sufficiently important to be worth worrying about.

Relations

Consider a universe having the form $U \times V$. A condition on such a universe is called a *binary relation*, or a *two-place predicate*. If α is a binary relation on $U \times V$, we write $\alpha(x, y)$ for the corresponding open sentence; x is a variable with domain U, y a variable with domain V, and (x, y) a variable with domain $U \times V$. The extension of α in $U \times V$ is a subset of $U \times V$; if it is not void, the extension of α in $U \times V$ is some collection of ordered couples each having first component in U and second component in V. (We have no right to presume that such a subset is itself the cartesian product of any pair of sets.) The subset of U whose members are those appearing as first component of some couple in the extension of α is called the *domain of the relation* α; the corresponding subset of V each of whose members appears as second component of some couple in the extension of α is called the *range of the relation* α. (Neither the domain nor the range of a relation can be void unless its extension is void, in which case all three are void.) Note that the domain of a variable and the domain of a relation are quite different things—they must never be confused. We examine some examples to illustrate these terms and to introduce the notion of the *graph of a relation*.

A Finite Example

Suppose $U = \{a_1, a_2, a_3\}$ and $V = \{b_1, b_2, b_3, b_4\}$. Then $U \times V$ has twelve members $(a_1, b_1), (a_1, b_2), \ldots, (a_3, b_4)$. Descartes' scheme may be adapted to depict the set $U \times V$, even though no members of U or V need be "numbers." We line up the members of U and V (in any order we choose) along a pair of lines, one—for U—horizontal, the other—for V—vertical.

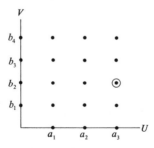

The members of $U \times V$ we represent by dots arranged in columns above members of U and in rows to the right of members of V (see figure). Each such dot represents that member of $U \times V$ whose first component is named directly below it on the U-line and whose second component is named directly to its left on the V-line. For example, the dot circled in the diagram above represents the couple (a_3, b_2). Now a relation on $U \times V$ may be represented by a subset of $U \times V$, and any subset of $U \times V$ may be depicted

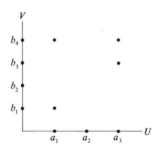

graphically by drawing only those dots which represent members of the subset. One such subset is shown in the accompanying figure: its members are (a_1, b_1), (a_1, b_4), (a_3, b_3), (a_3, b_4). If α is a relation whose extension in $\{a_1, a_2, a_3\} \times \{b_1, b_2, b_3, b_4\}$ is the subset

$$\{(a_1, b_1), (a_1, b_4), (a_3, b_3), (a_3, b_4)\},$$

the domain of α is $\{a_1, a_3\}$ and its range is $\{b_1, b_3, b_4\}$. If Ext α, Dom α, Ran α denote, respectively, the extension, the domain, and the range of α in $U \times V$, note—in particular—that Ext $\alpha \neq$ (Dom α) $\times$ (Ran α): the product contains (a_1, b_3) and (a_3, b_1), neither of which belong to Ext α. Note also that, although (Dom α) $\subseteq U$ and (Ran α) $\subseteq V$, neither (Dom α) $= U$ nor (Ran α) $= V$: $a_2 \in U$, but $a_2 \notin$ (Dom α), $b_2 \in V$, but $b_2 \notin$ (Ran α). The picture drawn above representing Ext α is called a *graph* of α.

This example might represent a situation of the following kind. Suppose U is a set of three men, V is a set of four women, and α is the relation *marriage* on $U \times V$. Thus we would read the open sentence $\alpha(x, y)$ as *x is a husband of y*. Relative to the universe $U \times V$, a_2 is a bachelor and b_2 a spinster, while b_4, a_1, and a_3 are bigamists.

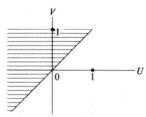

Another Example

Suppose U and V are both the set of real numbers. (This is Descartes' case.) Let $\alpha(x, y)$ be $x \leq y$. Arranging the members of U, V on the reference lines in their "customary order," Ext α is represented by a "half-plane": the graph of α contains all points on the line whose equation is $x = y$ and all points to the left of this line (see figure). Both Dom α and Ran α

are the set of all real numbers. These examples should make it quite clear that Ext α is not characterized by Dom α and Ran α alone: the latter determine only what parts of U and V, respectively, figure in Ext α. One must know much more than just Dom α and Ran α in order to decide whether or not a given couple (a, b) belongs to Ext α. Dom α and Ran α are only the "projections" of Ext α on U and V, respectively.

EXERCISES

1. Let $U = V = \{0, 1, 2, 3, 4, 5\}$. For each of the following relations on $U \times V$, sketch a graph and determine the domain and the range of the relation.

α_1:	$x - y = 0$,	α_2:	$x + y = 5$,
α_3:	$x + y = 0$,	α_4:	$xy = 4$,
α_5:	$y = x^2$,	α_6:	$x = y^2$,
α_7:	$x = xy$,	α_8:	$xy = yx$,
α_9:	$y < x^2$,	α_{10}:	$(y = x^2) \Rightarrow (y < x^2)$,
α_{11}:	$(y = x^2) \Rightarrow (y = x)$,	α_{12}:	$(y = x^2) \Rightarrow (y \neq x)$,
α_{13}:	$x = 2$,	α_{14}:	$x = x^2$,
α_{15}:	$(x - 1)y = 0$,	α_{16}:	$(y - 1)x = 0$,
α_{17}:	x is a factor of y.		

2. For each relation in Exercise 1, describe, or sketch, the graphs of the following sets

$$(\text{Dom }\alpha) \times (\text{Ran }\alpha), \qquad U \times (\text{Ran }\alpha), \qquad (\text{Dom }\alpha) \times V,$$

and observe that

$$(\text{Ext }\alpha) \subseteq (\text{Dom }\alpha) \times (\text{Ran }\alpha) \subseteq [U \times (\text{Ran }\alpha)] \cap [(\text{Dom }\alpha) \times V].$$

3. If α is a relation on $U \times V$, the graph of $\tilde{\alpha}$ is the set of points in the graph of $U \times V$ not in the graph of α. Give examples of finite U and V and relations α, $\tilde{\alpha}$ for which

$$U = \text{Dom }\alpha \qquad \text{but} \qquad V \neq \text{Ran }\tilde{\alpha},$$
$$U \neq \text{Dom }\alpha \qquad \text{but} \qquad V = \text{Ran }\tilde{\alpha},$$
$$U = \text{Dom }\alpha \qquad \text{and} \qquad V = \text{Ran }\tilde{\alpha}.$$

Try to find an example for the other combination:

$$U \neq \text{Dom }\alpha \qquad \text{and} \qquad V \neq \text{Ran }\tilde{\alpha}.$$

4. Pairs of relations such as α_5 and α_6, or α_{15} and α_{16} (in Exercise 1), are called *inverse pairs*: α_5 and α_6 are called *inverses* of each other, as are α_{15} and α_{16}. Their open sentences differ from each other merely by having x and y interchanged. Other examples of inverse pairs are

x is a parent of y, x is a child of y;

x is a husband of y, x is a wife of y.

Observe that for such a pair, the roles of U and V are reversed. Thus the last pair involves a set of men and a set of women: for the first one, U is the set of men and V the set of women, but for the second, U is the set of women and V the set of men. In particular, then, if α and α^* are a pair of inverse relations,

$$\text{Dom } \alpha = \text{Ran } \alpha^*, \qquad \text{Ran } \alpha = \text{Dom } \alpha^*.$$

Describe or sketch the graph of the inverse of each of the relations $\alpha_1, \ldots, \alpha_{17}$ of Exercise 1.

Quantification

Suppose that the universe $\mathfrak{U}$ is the product $U \times V$ of two sets and that α is a condition on $\mathfrak{U}$. We also say, as above, that α is a relation on $U \times V$; and if x and y are variables with domains U, V, respectively, we call (x, y) a variable with domain $U \times V$. If we write, simply, $\mathbf{x} = (x, y)$, with $\mathbf{x}$ a variable on $\mathfrak{U}$ and ignore the special structure of $\mathfrak{U}$ as a product $U \times V$, we can form the closed sentences

$$(\forall \mathbf{x} \in \mathfrak{U})\alpha(\mathbf{x}) \qquad \text{and} \qquad (\exists \mathbf{x} \in \mathfrak{U})\alpha(\mathbf{x}).$$

This, of course, is just what we did in Section 1. Taking note of the special structure of $\mathfrak{U}$, we might rewrite these statements as follows:

$$(\forall (x, y) \in U \times V)\alpha(x, y)$$

and

$$(\exists (x, y) \in U \times V)\alpha(x, y).$$

[Since $\mathbf{x} = (x, y)$, a purist may prefer to see $\alpha((x, y))$ for $\alpha(\mathbf{x})$. However, we shall regard the use of the extra pair of parentheses as one of those luxuries we can very well do without.] A little further on we shall write each of these statements in two other ways.

The one new idea we exploit here is this: if α is a relation on $U \times V$, we regard the four expressions

$$(\forall y \in V)\alpha(x, y), \qquad (\exists y \in V)\alpha(x, y)$$

and

$$(\forall x \in U)\alpha(x, y), \qquad (\exists x \in U)\alpha(x, y)$$

as open sentences—the first two representing conditions on U, the last two conditions on V. If we close each of these four open sentences with either a universal or an existential quantifier on the respective universes, we get the following list of eight statements:

$$\begin{array}{ll}
(\forall x \in U)(\forall y \in V)\alpha(x, y), & (\exists x \in U)(\forall y \in V)\alpha(x, y), \\
(\forall x \in U)(\exists y \in V)\alpha(x, y), & (\exists x \in U)(\exists y \in V)\alpha(x, y), \\
(\forall y \in V)(\forall x \in U)\alpha(x, y), & (\exists y \in V)(\forall x \in U)\alpha(x, y), \\
(\forall y \in V)(\exists x \in U)\alpha(x, y), & (\exists y \in V)(\exists x \in U)\alpha(x, y).
\end{array}$$

We give an example. Suppose $\alpha(x, y)$ is *x loves y*, with U and V both the set of people. The four open sentences are then

$(\forall y \in V)\alpha(x, y)$: *x loves everyone*
$(\exists y \in V)\alpha(x, y)$: *x loves someone*
$(\forall x \in U)\alpha(x, y)$: *y is loved by everybody*
$(\exists x \in U)\alpha(x, y)$: *y is loved by somebody*

and the eight closed sentences are (suppressing U, V):

$(\forall x)(\forall y)\alpha(x, y)$: *Everybody loves everyone*
$(\exists x)(\forall y)\alpha(x, y)$: *Somebody loves everyone*
$(\forall x)(\exists y)\alpha(x, y)$: *Each person loves someone*
$(\exists x)(\exists y)\alpha(x, y)$: *Somebody loves someone*
$(\forall y)(\forall x)\alpha(x, y)$: *Everyone is loved by everybody*
$(\exists y)(\forall x)\alpha(x, y)$: *Someone is loved by everybody*
$(\forall y)(\exists x)\alpha(x, y)$: *Each person is loved by somebody*
$(\exists y)(\exists x)\alpha(x, y)$: *Someone is loved by somebody.*

These eight statements are by no means "independent": indeed we undertake shortly the project of determining just which ones "formally imply" others in the list. The results we shall establish are these: each of the following is a tautology,

$$(\forall x)(\forall y)\pi(x, y) \iff (\forall y)(\forall x)\pi(x, y)$$
$$(\exists x)(\exists y)\pi(x, y) \iff (\exists y)(\exists x)\pi(x, y),$$

$$(\exists x)(\forall y)\pi(x, y) \implies (\forall y)(\exists x)\pi(x, y)$$
$$(\exists y)(\forall x)\pi(x, y) \implies (\forall x)(\exists y)\pi(x, y),$$

$$(\forall y)(\forall x)\pi(x, y) \implies (\exists x)(\forall y)\pi(x, y)$$
$$(\forall x)(\exists y)\pi(x, y) \implies (\exists y)(\exists x)\pi(x, y),$$

$$(\forall x)(\forall y)\pi(x, y) \implies (\exists y)(\forall x)\pi(x, y)$$
$$(\forall y)(\exists x)\pi(x, y) \implies (\exists x)(\exists y)\pi(x, y),$$

where, for the third pair, $U \neq \emptyset$, and for the fourth, $V \neq \emptyset$. Observe that the first pair are two-way implications, so that a pair of like quantifiers (both universal or both existential) may be interchanged. But all the others are only one-way implications; in particular, the second pair shows that the order of a pair of "unlike" quantifiers is critical. The difference, which can be illustrated by the examples

Someone is called the father of everybody.
Everybody has someone who is called his father.

is quite significant.

The tautologies above are all summarized in the following "mnemonic octagon":

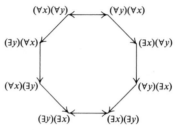

In the "one-dimensional" case we interpret the quantifiers as follows:

$(\forall x \in U)\alpha(x)$:   *The extension of α is all of U.*

$(\exists x \in U)\alpha(x)$:   *The extension of α is not empty.*

In "two dimensions" with universe $U \times V$, we have eight "quantifiers" instead of just two, and, consequently, a greater number of distinctions are involved. Consider the graph of the entire product $U \times V$ which, for simplicity, we illustrate in the case $U = \{a_1, a_2, a_3, a_4\}$, $V = \{b_1, b_2, b_3\}$.

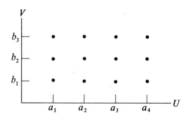

This graph may be partitioned into *columns* (corresponding to each of the members of U), or into *rows* (corresponding to each of the members of V).

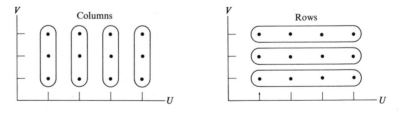

If α is a relation on $U \times V$, its graph is some subset of the "full graph" and it may also be partitioned into columns or rows corresponding to the individual members of U or V. Referring to the rows and columns of the graph of α we interpret the four open sentences obtained by prefixing just one quantifier to $\alpha(x, y)$ as follows:

In the graph of α,

$(\forall y \in V)\alpha(x, y)$:   *Column x is full.*

$(\exists y \in V)\alpha(x, y)$:   *Column x is not empty.*

$(\forall x \in U)\alpha(x, y)$:   *Row y is full.*

$(\exists x \in U)\alpha(x, y)$:   *Row y is not empty.*

The closed sentences with double quantifiers then yield

$(\forall x)(\forall y)\alpha(x, y)$:   *Each column is full.*

$(\exists x)(\forall y)\alpha(x, y)$:   *Some column is full.*

$(\forall x)(\exists y)\alpha(x, y)$:   *No column is empty.*

$(\exists x)(\exists y)\alpha(x, y)$:   *Some column is not empty.*

$(\forall y)(\forall x)\alpha(x, y)$:   *Each row is full.*

$(\exists y)(\forall x)\alpha(x, y)$:   *Some row is full.*

$(\forall y)(\exists x)\alpha(x, y)$:   *No row is empty.*

$(\exists y)(\exists x)\alpha(x, y)$:   *Some row is not empty.*

EXERCISE

1. For each of the 17 binary relations in Exercise 1, page 117, determine which of the 8 closed sentences with double quantifiers are true and which are false.

When we work in three dimensions, we have a much greater variety of quantifiers than we have in one or two dimensions. Suppose $U \times V \times W$ is the set of ordered triples (u, v, w) with $u \in U$, $v \in V$, $w \in W$, and suppose α is a relation on $U \times V \times W$. (Such a relation is called a *ternary* relation, to indicate that there are three variables.) Prefixing a single quantifier to the open sentence $\alpha(x, y, z)$, we obtain six binary relations:

$$(\forall x \in U)\alpha(x, y, z), \qquad (\exists x \in U)\alpha(x, y, z),$$
$$(\forall y \in V)\alpha(x, y, z), \qquad (\exists y \in V)\alpha(x, y, z),$$
$$(\forall z \in W)\alpha(x, y, z), \qquad (\exists z \in W)\alpha(x, y, z).$$

Double quantifiers give twenty-four (one-place) conditions:

$(\forall y)(\forall x)\alpha(x, y, z)$,	$(\forall x)(\forall z)\alpha(x, y, z)$,	$(\forall x)(\exists y)\alpha(x, y, z)$,
$(\exists y)(\forall x)\alpha(x, y, z)$,	$(\exists x)(\forall z)\alpha(x, y, z)$,	$(\exists x)(\exists y)\alpha(x, y, z)$,
$(\forall z)(\forall x)\alpha(x, y, z)$,	$(\forall y)(\forall z)\alpha(x, y, z)$,	$(\forall z)(\exists y)\alpha(x, y, z)$,
$(\exists z)(\forall x)\alpha(x, y, z)$,	$(\exists y)(\forall z)\alpha(x, y, z)$,	$(\exists z)(\exists y)\alpha(x, y, z)$,
$(\forall x)(\forall y)\alpha(x, y, z)$,	$(\forall y)(\exists x)\alpha(x, y, z)$,	$(\forall x)(\exists z)\alpha(x, y, z)$,
$(\exists x)(\forall y)\alpha(x, y, z)$,	$(\exists y)(\exists x)\alpha(x, y, z)$,	$(\exists x)(\exists z)\alpha(x, y, z)$,
$(\forall z)(\forall y)\alpha(x, y, z)$,	$(\forall z)(\exists x)\alpha(x, y, z)$	$(\forall y)(\exists z)\alpha(x, y, z)$,
$(\exists z)(\forall y)\alpha(x, y, z)$,	$(\exists z)(\exists x)\alpha(x, y, z)$,	$(\exists y)(\exists z)\alpha(x, y, z)$,

and—for each of these—there are two ways to prefix a third quantifier. Thus, in all, there are forty-eight quantifiers in three dimensions, corresponding to the eight quantifiers in two dimensions and the two quantifiers in one dimension. In n dimensions, the number of quantifiers is $2^n(n!)$.

In three or more dimensions, interpretations based on the graph of α are possible, analogous to the interpretations we have discussed in the cases of one and two dimensions. It should be clear that their complexity grows much more rapidly than the number of dimensions; we leave their formulation to the interested reader. In the next section we consider more efficient ways to handle multiple quantifiers. At this point we concentrate on some examples which illustrate the analysis of the structure of sentences with multiple quantifiers.

Congruent triangles are similar:

$$(\forall x)(\forall y)[\alpha(x, y) \implies \beta(x, y)].$$

Here we take U and V to be the set of all triangles, $\alpha(x, y)$ to be x *is congruent to* y, and $\beta(x, y)$ to be x *is similar to* y.

No one can learn anything he already knows:

$$(\forall x)(\forall y)[\alpha(x, y) \implies \tilde{\beta}(x, y)].$$

Here we take for U the set of people, V the collection of knowledge, with $\alpha(x, y)$ for x *knows* y, and $\beta(x, y)$ for x *can learn* y.

No one who knows everything can learn anything:

$$(\forall x)[(\forall y)\alpha(x, y) \implies (\forall y)\tilde{\beta}(x, y)].$$

Here U, V, α, β are the same as in the preceding example.

If everybody knew everything, then nobody could learn anything:

$$(\forall x)(\forall y)\alpha(x, y) \implies (\forall x)(\forall y)\tilde{\beta}(x, y).$$

Same U, V, α, β.

All hope abandon, ye who enter:

$$(\forall x)[\alpha(x) \implies (\forall y)\beta(x, y)].$$

U: people, V: hope, $\alpha(x)$: x *enters*, $\beta(x, y)$: x *abandons* y.

Hard is his harte that loveth nought in May:

$$(\forall x)(\forall y)\{\alpha(x, y) \wedge [(\forall z)\tilde{\gamma}(y, z)] \implies \beta(x)\}.$$

U: hearts, V: people, W: people, $\alpha(x, y)$: x *belongs to* y, $\beta(x)$: x *is hard*, $\gamma(y, z)$: y *loves* z *in May*.

Anyone who can win all the marbles everybody has, gets to pick all the dolls he wants:

$$(\forall x)\{(\forall y)(\forall z)[\alpha(y, z) \Rightarrow \beta(x, y)] \Rightarrow (\forall u)[\gamma(x, u) \Rightarrow \delta(x, u)]\}.$$

$x \in U$: people, $y \in V$: marbles, $z \in W$: people, $u \in A$: dolls, $\alpha(y, z)$: *y belongs to z*, $\beta(x, y)$: *x can win y*, $\gamma(x, u)$: *x wants u*, $\delta(x, u)$: *x can pick u*.

EXERCISES

Parse the sentences in Exercises 1 through 24.

1. Everybody can do something well.
2. Some courses are required for all students.
3. Every student is required to take a foreign language.
4. A woman's work is never done.
5. There is someone whom nobody ever believes.
6. Some people believe everything everybody tells them.
7. Some people believe nothing anybody tells them.
8. Nobody can remember everything he knows.
9. Anyone who knows all the theorems can work all the problems.
10. Nobody likes doing anything he can neither do well nor avoid completely.
11. If everybody can work some of these problems, nobody can work them all.
12. People who live in glass houses should never throw stones.
13. Wherever there is smoke there is fire.
14. A [i.e., every] horse's tail is an animal's tail.
15. All things come to those who wait.
16. A rolling stone gathers no moss.
17. No one, who can learn everything, knows anything.
18. Nobody knows anything if everybody can learn everything.
19. Each even number greater than 2 is the sum of two primes.
20. You can fool all the people some of the time, and some of the people all the time, but you cannot fool all the people all of the time.
21. If any one anything lacks,
    He'll find it all ready in stacks,
       If he'll only look in
       On the resident Djinn,
    Number seventy, Simmery Axe!
22. Everyone meets somebody he will like at least as well as anybody he will ever meet.

23. There is a sentence like none any student was ever asked to parse in any class in grammar.

24. Neither slavery nor involuntary servitude, except as a punishment for crime whereof the party shall have been duly convicted, shall exist within the United States, or any place subject to their jurisdiction.

25. Suppose $V = \{a, b\}$. Then

$$(\forall x)(\forall y)\pi(x, y) \quad \text{is} \quad (\forall x)[\pi(x, a) \wedge \pi(x, b)],$$

$$(\forall y)(\exists x)\pi(x, y) \quad \text{is} \quad [(\exists x)\pi(x, a)] \wedge [(\exists x)\pi(x, b)],$$

for example. Rewrite the other six similarly and, for this special case, prove all the tautologies indicated in the octagon.

26. We may extend De Morgan's tautologies to expressions with more that one quantifier by working on the quantifiers one at a time, as follows:

$$\sim[(\forall x)(\exists y)\pi(x, y)] \iff (\exists x)[\sim(\exists y)\pi(x, y)]$$

$$\iff (\exists x)(\forall y)\bar{\pi}(x, y).$$

Using this idea show that the tautologies represented by pairs of opposite (i.e., parallel) sides of the octagon are contrapositives of each other. (This observation halves the problem we face of proving all of them.)

27. Use the method in Exercise 26 to negate your symbolic versions of the sentences in Exercises 1 through 24, and give an English version for each of these negations.

28. If α and α^* are a pair of inverse relations (cf. Exercise 4, page 117), we have

$$(\forall x)(\forall y)\alpha(x, y) \iff (\forall y)(\forall x)\alpha^*(x, y),$$

$$(\forall x)(\exists y)\alpha(x, y) \iff (\forall y)(\exists x)\alpha^*(x, y),$$

etc. Show how this observation can also be used to halve the problem of proving all the tautologies indicated in the octagon.

The grammatical complexity of the sentences considered in this section is comparable to that of a great many of the statements one encounters in mathematics—at all levels, from the most elementary to the most advanced. In the next chapter we consider some examples of mathematical proofs which, as we shall see, reduce ultimately to the consideration of just such grammatical complexities. Hence the conclusion that the subteties of grammar play a fundamental role in the understanding of proofs and, consequently, in the understanding of mathematics itself.

The examples considered in the next chapter are all concerned with the algebra of number systems. Here we parse some of the more interesting sentences one encounters in a calculus course.

In the following examples, f is a real-valued function whose domain is a set of real numbers, I is an interval of real numbers, a is a fixed member of I, and P is the set of positive real numbers. I is a subset of the domain of f, except for the first example, where we require only that $I - \{a\}$ be a subset of the domain of f.

Limit: $\lim_a f = l$,

$$(\forall \epsilon \in P)(\exists \delta \in P)(\forall x \in I)\{(0 < |x - a| < \delta) \Rightarrow (|f(x) - l| < \epsilon)\}.$$

Continuity at a Point: f is continuous at a,

$$(\forall \epsilon \in P)(\exists \delta \in P)(\forall x \in I)\{(|x - a| < \delta) \Rightarrow (|f(x) - f(a)| < \epsilon)\}.$$

Continuity on an Interval: f is continuous on I,

$$(\forall x' \in I)(\forall \epsilon \in P)(\exists \delta \in P)(\forall x \in I)\{(|x - x'| < \delta)$$
$$\Rightarrow (|f(x) - f(x')| < \epsilon)\}.$$

Uniform Continuity: f is uniformly continuous on I,

$$(\forall \epsilon \in P)(\exists \delta \in P)(\forall x' \in I)(\forall x \in I)\{(|x - x'| < \delta)$$
$$\Rightarrow (|f(x) - f(x')| < \epsilon)\}.$$

(Observe that the last pair differ only in the order of the quantifiers.)

Similar examples occur in the theory of infinite series: here P is the set of positive real numbers, N is the set of natural numbers, I is an interval of real numbers, $\{a_n\}$ is a sequence of real numbers, and $\{f_n(x)\}$ is a sequence of real functions, each of which is defined on the interval I.

Cauchy's Criterion for Convergence of $\sum a_n$:

$$(\forall \epsilon \in P)(\exists k \in N)(\forall n \in N)\{(n > k) \Rightarrow (|a_n - a_k| < \epsilon)\}.$$

Convergence of $\sum f_n(x)$ on I:

$$(\forall x \in I)(\forall \epsilon \in P)(\exists k \in N)(\forall n \in N)\{(n > k)$$
$$\Rightarrow (|f_n(x) - f_k(x)| < \epsilon)\}.$$

Uniform Convergence of $\sum f_n(x)$ on I:

$$(\forall \epsilon \in P)(\exists k \in N)(\forall x \in I)(\forall n \in N)\{(n > k)$$
$$\Rightarrow (|f_n(x) - f_k(x)| < \epsilon)\}.$$

(Observe that the last pair differ only in the order of the quantifiers.)

In Chapter 4, we shall encounter some statements, just as complicated as any of these, which occur in the study of algebra.

EXERCISE

1. Negate each of the seven statements parsed above.

5. DERIVATION OF TAUTOLOGIES. INFERENCE

In this section we consider the derivation of tautologies with multiple quantifiers and examine some of the inference problems that can be solved with the means now at our disposal. There are more examples in the next chapter, where we consider some mathematical proofs. We begin with the octagon of two-dimensional quantifiers introduced in the last section.

Exploiting symmetries of the octagon (Exercises 26 and 28, page 124), we find that it is enough to get only three tautologies: one corresponding to any one of the four horizontal one-way arrows, either of the two vertical arrows, and any one of the four others. Two more simple ideas will let us settle the matter.

The first of these ideas is that quantifiers may be treated independently of one another. Consider for example

$$(\forall x)(\forall y)[\pi(x, y) \Rightarrow \rho(x, y)].$$

Leave the first quantifier alone and use change-of-scope tautologies C1 and D3 on the second:

$$(\forall x)(\forall y)[\pi(x, y) \Rightarrow \rho(x, y)] \Rightarrow (\forall x)[(\forall y)\pi(x, y) \Rightarrow (\forall y)\rho(x, y)],$$
$$(\forall x)(\forall y)[\pi(x, y) \Rightarrow \rho(x, y)] \Rightarrow (\forall x)[(\exists y)\pi(x, y) \Rightarrow (\exists y)\rho(x, y)].$$

Here we simply ignore the x's in the scope of $(\forall y)$, formally treating $\pi(x, y)$ and $\rho(x, y)$ as if they were conditions on V. Next we move $(\forall x)$ in too, using C1 and D3 again, twice each:

$$(\forall x)[(\forall y)\pi(x, y) \Rightarrow (\forall y)\rho(x, y)]$$
$$\Rightarrow [(\forall x)(\forall y)\pi(x, y) \Rightarrow (\forall x)(\forall y)\rho(x, y)],$$
$$(\forall x)[(\forall y)\pi(x, y) \Rightarrow (\forall y)\rho(x, y)]$$
$$\Rightarrow [(\exists x)(\forall y)\pi(x, y) \Rightarrow (\exists x)(\forall y)\rho(x, y)],$$
$$(\forall x)[(\exists y)\pi(x, y) \Rightarrow (\exists y)\rho(x, y)]$$
$$\Rightarrow [(\forall x)(\exists y)\pi(x, y) \Rightarrow (\forall x)(\exists y)\rho(x, y)],$$
$$(\forall x)[(\exists y)\pi(x, y) \Rightarrow (\exists y)\rho(x, y)]$$
$$\Rightarrow [(\exists x)(\exists y)\pi(x, y) \Rightarrow (\exists x)(\exists y)\rho(x, y)].$$

Combining both steps, we conclude that

$$(\forall x)(\forall y)[\pi(x, y) \Rightarrow \rho(x, y)]$$

tautologically implies all four of the following:

$$(\forall x)(\forall y)\pi(x, y) \Rightarrow (\forall x)(\forall y)\rho(x, y),$$
$$(\exists x)(\forall y)\pi(x, y) \Rightarrow (\exists x)(\forall y)\rho(x, y),$$
$$(\forall x)(\exists y)\pi(x, y) \Rightarrow (\forall x)(\exists y)\rho(x, y),$$
$$(\exists x)(\exists y)\pi(x, y) \Rightarrow (\exists x)(\exists y)\rho(x, y).$$

We leave as an exercise the question of providing interpretations for the results of these formal manipulations.

The second idea is a little more subtle. Write

$$\sigma(y) = (\exists x)\pi(x, y).$$

We have said that σ is to be interpreted as a condition on V. (Indeed, the extension of σ in V is just Ran π.) But we now interpret σ to be a relation on $U \times V$: as such it is "degenerate"; a couple (a, b) in $U \times V$ satisfies σ if and only if $b \in$ Ran π, a being any member of U. So the extension of σ in $U \times V$ is the product $U \times$ (Ran π). Observe, however, that

$$(\text{Ext } \pi) \subseteq U \times (\text{Ran } \pi),$$

which, by identifying $(\forall x \in U)(\forall y \in V)$ with $\big(\forall(x, y) \in U \times V\big)$, we translate as follows:

$$(\forall x)(\forall y)[\pi(x, y) \Rightarrow \sigma(y)] \quad \text{is a tautology.}$$

Combining both of these ideas, we conclude that each of the following is a tautology:

$$(\forall x)(\forall y)\pi(x, y) \Rightarrow (\forall y)\sigma(y) \quad [U \neq \varnothing],$$
$$(\exists x)(\forall y)\pi(x, y) \Rightarrow (\forall y)\sigma(y),$$
$$(\forall x)(\exists y)\pi(x, y) \Rightarrow (\exists y)\sigma(y) \quad [U \neq \varnothing],$$
$$(\exists x)(\exists y)\pi(x, y) \Rightarrow (\exists y)\sigma(y).$$

Finally, we replace $\sigma(y)$ by $(\exists x)\pi(x, y)$:

$$(\forall x)(\forall y)\pi(x, y) \Rightarrow (\forall y)(\exists x)\pi(x, y) \quad [U \neq \varnothing],$$
$$(\exists x)(\forall y)\pi(x, y) \Rightarrow (\forall y)(\exists x)\pi(x, y),$$
$$(\forall x)(\exists y)\pi(x, y) \Rightarrow (\exists y)(\exists x)\pi(x, y) \quad [U \neq \varnothing],$$
$$(\exists x)(\exists y)\pi(x, y) \Rightarrow (\exists y)(\exists x)\pi(x, y).$$

Of these four, the last three are just what we need; and we are done!

EXERCISES

1. Use

$$(\text{Dom } \pi) = \{x \in U : (\exists y \in V)\pi(x, y)\},$$
$$(\text{Ran } \pi) = \{y \in V : (\exists x \in U)\pi(x, y)\}$$

(and corresponding identifications for ρ instead of π) to provide interpretations for

$$(\forall x)(\forall y)[\pi(x, y) \Rightarrow \rho(x, y)] \Rightarrow (\forall x)[(\exists y)\pi(x, y) \Rightarrow (\exists y)\rho(x, y)],$$
$$(\forall y)(\forall x)[\pi(x, y) \Rightarrow \rho(x, y)] \Rightarrow (\forall y)[(\exists x)\pi(x, y) \Rightarrow (\exists x)\rho(x, y)],$$
$$(\forall x)(\forall y)[\pi(x, y) \Rightarrow \rho(x, y)] \Rightarrow [(\forall x)(\exists y)\pi(x, y) \Rightarrow (\forall x)(\exists y)\rho(x, y)],$$
$$(\forall x)(\forall y)[\pi(x, y) \Rightarrow \rho(x, y)] \Rightarrow [(\exists x)(\exists y)\pi(x, y) \Rightarrow (\exists x)(\exists y)\rho(x, y)].$$

2. Using $p \Rightarrow q \equiv \tilde{p} \vee q$, rewrite

$$(\exists x)(\forall y)\pi(x, y) \Rightarrow (\forall y)(\exists x)\pi(x, y)$$
$$(\exists y)(\forall x)\pi(x, y) \Rightarrow (\forall x)(\exists y)\pi(x, y),$$

and give interpretations in terms of Dom π, Ran π, etc.

3. Describe the graphs of the sets

$$\{x \in U : (\forall y \in V)\pi(x, y)\}, \qquad \{y \in V : (\forall x \in U)\pi(x, y)\}$$

and use them to give interpretations of

$$(\forall x)(\forall y)[\pi(x, y) \Rightarrow \rho(x, y)] \Rightarrow (\forall x)[(\forall y)\pi(x, y) \Rightarrow (\forall y)\rho(x, y)],$$
$$(\forall y)(\forall x)[\pi(x, y) \Rightarrow \rho(x, y)] \Rightarrow (\forall y)[(\forall x)\pi(x, y) \Rightarrow (\forall x)\rho(x, y)],$$
$$(\forall x)(\forall y)[\pi(x, y) \Rightarrow \rho(x, y)] \Rightarrow [(\forall x)(\forall y)\pi(x, y) \Rightarrow (\forall x)(\forall y)\rho(x, y)],$$
$$(\forall x)(\forall y)[\pi(x, y) \Rightarrow \rho(x, y)] \Rightarrow [(\exists x)(\forall y)\pi(x, y) \Rightarrow (\exists x)(\forall y)\rho(x, y)],$$

and

$$(\exists x)(\forall y)\pi(x, y) \Rightarrow (\forall y)(\exists x)\pi(x, y),$$
$$(\exists y)(\forall x)\pi(x, y) \Rightarrow (\forall x)(\exists y)\pi(x, y).$$

4. Derive the following tautologies ($U \neq \emptyset$, $V \neq \emptyset$):

$$(\exists x)(\forall y)[\pi(x) \wedge \rho(y)] \Leftrightarrow (\forall y)(\exists x)[\pi(x) \wedge \rho(y)],$$
$$(\exists x)(\forall y)[\pi(x) \vee \rho(y)] \Leftrightarrow (\forall y)(\exists x)[\pi(x) \vee \rho(y)],$$
$$(\exists x)(\forall y)[\pi(x) \Rightarrow \rho(y)] \Leftrightarrow (\forall y)(\exists x)[\pi(x) \Rightarrow \rho(y)].$$

5. Suppose $\rho(x, y, z) = \pi(x, z, y)$ and derive the tautologies

$$(\forall x)[(\forall y)(\forall z)\pi(x, y, z) \Rightarrow (\forall z)(\forall y)\rho(x, y, z)],$$
$$(\forall x)[(\exists y)(\forall z)\pi(x, y, z) \Rightarrow (\exists z)(\forall y)\rho(x, y, z)],$$
$$(\forall x)[(\forall y)(\exists z)\pi(x, y, z) \Rightarrow (\forall z)(\exists y)\rho(x, y, z)].$$

[Compare with Exercise 28, page 124.]

6. Suppose $V = W \neq \emptyset$ and derive the tautologies

$$(\forall x)[(\forall y)\pi(x, y) \Rightarrow (\forall z)\pi(x, z)],$$
$$(\forall x)[(\exists y)\pi(x, y) \Rightarrow (\exists z)\pi(x, z)].$$

[*Hint:* Define a degenerate ternary relation $\pi(x, y, z)$ by putting $\pi(x, y, z) = \pi(x, y)$, and use the tautologies in Exercise 5.]

Inference

We now consider some inference problems involving statements with several quantifiers. Some are quite trivial:

Everybody but the villain lives happily ever after, but some of the characters are so obnoxious nobody could put up with them.

∴. *Everybody but the villain lives happily ever after.*

In spite of all the quantifiers, this is just like our very first (and most trivial) example of an inference.

Some less trivial examples are syllogisms. If $\mathfrak{U} = U \times V$, for example, then $(\forall x \in U)(\forall y \in V)$ and $(\exists x \in U)(\exists y \in V)$ are just $(\forall \mathbf{x} \in \mathfrak{U})$ and

$(\exists \mathbf{x} \in \mathfrak{U})$, respectively [here, again, $\mathbf{x} = (x, y)$]. Thus, for instance,

$$(\forall x)(\forall y)[\beta(x, y) \Rightarrow \gamma(x, y)],$$
$$(\forall x)(\forall y)[\alpha(x, y) \Rightarrow \beta(x, y)],$$
$$\therefore (\forall x)(\forall y)[\alpha(x, y) \Rightarrow \gamma(x, y)]$$

is simply BARBARA, on the universe $U \times V$; and

$$(\exists x)(\exists y)[\beta(x, y) \wedge \tilde{\gamma}(x, y)],$$
$$(\forall x)(\forall y)[\beta(x, y) \Rightarrow \alpha(x, y)],$$
$$\therefore (\exists x)(\exists y)[\alpha(x, y) \wedge \tilde{\gamma}(x, y)]$$

is BOCARDO on $U \times V$.

There are some variants on this idea. Consider, for example, the pattern

$$(\forall y)(\exists x)[\beta(y) \Rightarrow \gamma(x, y)],$$
$$(\forall y)(\forall x)[\alpha(y) \Rightarrow \tilde{\gamma}(x, y)],$$
$$\therefore (\forall y)[\alpha(y) \Rightarrow \tilde{\beta}(y)].$$

From the premises we can infer

$$(\forall y)[(\forall x)\tilde{\gamma}(x, y) \Rightarrow \tilde{\beta}(y)],$$
$$(\forall y)[\alpha(y) \Rightarrow (\forall x)\tilde{\gamma}(x, y)],$$

and the conclusion follows by CELARENT (with α as minor term, β as major term, $(\forall x)\tilde{\gamma}(x, y)$ as middle term, and V as universe).

There are other patterns which look something like syllogisms but are not. Consider

$$(\forall x)(\exists y)[\beta(x, y) \wedge \gamma(x, y)],$$
$$(\forall x)(\forall y)[\beta(x, y) \Rightarrow \alpha(x, y)],$$
$$\therefore (\forall x)(\exists y)[\alpha(x, y) \wedge \gamma(x, y)].$$

[This would be DISAMIS if the quantifiers in the first premise and the conclusion were $(\exists x)(\exists y)$.] We can justify this inference using the tautologies

$(\forall x)(\forall y)[\pi(x, y) \Rightarrow \rho(x, y)]$
$$\Rightarrow (\forall x)(\forall y)[\pi(x, y) \wedge \sigma(x, y) \Rightarrow \rho(x, y) \wedge \sigma(x, y)]$$

(Exercise 2, page 107) and

$(\forall x)(\forall y)[\pi(x, y) \wedge \sigma(x, y) \Rightarrow \rho(x, y) \wedge \sigma(x, y)]$
$$\Rightarrow \{(\forall x)(\exists y)[\pi(x, y) \wedge \sigma(x, y)] \Rightarrow (\forall x)(\exists y)[\rho(x, y) \wedge \sigma(x, y)]\}.$$

Moreover, we can transform the original pattern into a number of others using contraposition and conversion, just as we did with syllogisms themselves.

Example 1

Premises: *No bus driver likes any foreign car. All Alfas are foreign cars.*
Conclusion: *No bus driver likes any Alfa.*

Introduce universes U (people) and V (cars), conditions α (on U), β (on V), γ (on V):

$$\alpha(x):\quad x \text{ is a bus driver,}$$
$$\beta(y):\quad y \text{ is a foreign car,}$$
$$\gamma(y):\quad y \text{ is an Alfa}$$

and a relation δ on $U \times V$:

$$\delta(x, y):\quad x \text{ likes } y.$$

Then the premises are

(1) $(\forall x \in U)(\forall y \in V)[\alpha(x) \wedge \beta(y) \Rightarrow \tilde{\delta}(x, y)]$,

(2) $(\forall y \in V)[\gamma(y) \Rightarrow \beta(y)]$,

and the conclusion is

$$(\forall x \in U)(\forall y \in V)[\alpha(x) \wedge \gamma(y) \Rightarrow \tilde{\delta}(x, y)].$$

We start by rewriting the first premise:

$$(\forall x \in U)(\forall y \in V)\{\alpha(x) \Rightarrow [\beta(y) \Rightarrow \tilde{\delta}(x, y)]\}.$$

Since α is "degenerate on V," we may put this in the form

$$(\forall x \in U)\{\alpha(x) \Rightarrow (\forall y \in V)[\beta(y) \Rightarrow \tilde{\delta}(x, y)]\},$$

using change-of-scope tautology C1, whose converse is a tautology too in this case (cf. Exercise 1, page 106). Now let $A = (\text{Ext } \alpha) \subseteq U$ and restrict the external quantifier to A:

$$(\forall x \in A)(\forall y \in V)[\beta(y) \Rightarrow \tilde{\delta}(x, y)].$$

In the same way, the conclusion can be written

$$(\forall x \in A)(\forall y \in V)[\gamma(y) \Rightarrow \tilde{\delta}(x, y)].$$

This much of the argument could all have been avoided by a little cunning in selecting the universes to begin with: after all, the problem concerns bus drivers only. In any event we have reduced the problem to the following inference:

(1) $(\forall x \in A)(\forall y \in V)[\beta(y) \Rightarrow \tilde{\delta}(x, y)]$

(2) $(\forall y \in V)[\gamma(y) \Rightarrow \beta(y)]$

$$\therefore (\forall x \in A)(\forall y \in V)[\gamma(y) \Rightarrow \tilde{\delta}(x, y)].$$

From here on it is easy. Because the second premise is "independent of x" (i.e., degenerate on A) we may infer

$$(\forall x \in A)(\forall y \in V)[\gamma(y) \Rightarrow \beta(y)],$$

and the conclusion follows by CELARENT on $A \times V$.

Example 2

Premise: *Everyone who has children buys lollipops.*

Conclusion: *If there were no lollipops, then no one would have any children.*

Take U: people, V: people, and W: candy. Introduce conditions α (on V) and β (on W):

$$\alpha(y): \quad y \text{ is a child}$$
$$\beta(z): \quad z \text{ is a lollipop,}$$

and relations γ (on $U \times V$) and δ (on $U \times W$):

$$\gamma(x, y): \quad x \text{ has } y$$
$$\delta(x, z): \quad x \text{ buys } z.$$

For the premise we have

$$(\forall x \in U)\{(\exists y \in V)[\alpha(y) \wedge \gamma(x, y)] \Rightarrow (\exists z \in W)[\beta(z) \wedge \delta(x, z)]\},$$

and for the conclusion,

$$[\sim(\exists z \in W)\beta(z)] \Rightarrow (\forall x \in U)(\forall y \in V)[\gamma(x, y) \Rightarrow \tilde{\alpha}(y)],$$

or

$$(\exists x \in U)(\exists y \in V)[\alpha(y) \wedge \gamma(x, y)] \Rightarrow (\exists z \in W)\beta(z).$$

Observe, again, that α can be dropped: restrict the quantifiers on V to the subset A, where $A = (\text{Ext } \alpha) \subseteq V$. Then premise and conclusion become

$$(\forall x \in U)\{(\exists y \in A)\gamma(x, y) \Rightarrow (\exists z \in W)[\beta(z) \wedge \delta(x, z)]\},$$
$$\therefore (\exists x \in U)(\exists y \in A)\gamma(x, y) \Rightarrow (\exists z \in W)\beta(z).$$

Again, the rest is easy: the premise gives [D3]

$$(\exists x \in U)(\exists y \in A)\gamma(x, y) \Rightarrow (\exists x \in U)(\exists z \in W)[\beta(z) \wedge \delta(x, z)];$$

assume the hypothesis, $(\exists x \in U)(\exists y \in A)\gamma(x, y)$, and we get [T-4]

$$(\exists x \in U)(\exists z \in W)[\beta(z) \wedge \delta(x, z)];$$

hence [B2]

$$(\exists z \in W)\beta(z) \wedge (\exists x \in U)(\exists z \in W)\delta(x, z),$$

the last half of which we discard [T-2].

We consider one more example, of interest on historical grounds, because it illustrates one of the ways modern logic surpasses classical logic. Commenting on the inability of traditional logic to handle relations, which made it of little use in analyzing even the mathematics of Aristotle's day, De Morgan is supposed to have maintained that for nearly two thousand years logicians were unable to prove that a horse's tail is an animal's tail, given that horses are animals.

Example 3

Premise: *Horses are animals.*

Conclusion: *A horse's tail is an animal's tail.*

Suppose U is the set of living beings, for example, and V is some set containing things like tails. Consider conditions α, β on U:

$$\alpha(x): \quad x \text{ is a horse,}$$
$$\beta(x): \quad x \text{ is an animal}$$

and a relation γ on $U \times V$:

$$\gamma(x, y): \quad y \text{ is a tail of } x.$$

Then, given

$$(\forall x \in U)[\alpha(x) \Rightarrow \beta(x)],$$

we are to infer

$$(\forall y \in V)\{(\exists x \in U)[\alpha(x) \wedge \gamma(x, y)] \Rightarrow (\exists x \in U)[\beta(x) \wedge \gamma(x, y)]\}.$$

Because the premise is independent of y we can infer

$$(\forall y \in V)(\forall x \in U)[\alpha(x) \Rightarrow \beta(x)],$$

from which we may deduce (cf. Exercise 2, page 107)

$$(\forall y \in V)(\forall x \in U)[\alpha(x) \wedge \gamma(x, y) \Rightarrow \beta(x) \wedge \gamma(x, y)];$$

and with the change-of-scope tautology D3 we get what we want:

$$(\forall y \in V)\{(\exists x \in U)[\alpha(x) \wedge \gamma(x, y)] \Rightarrow (\exists x \in U)[\beta(x) \wedge \gamma(x, y)]\}.$$

This inference has an interesting geometrical interpretation. The crux of the argument can be represented by the tautology

$$(\forall x \in U)(\forall y \in V)[\pi(x, y) \Rightarrow \rho(x, y)]$$
$$\Rightarrow (\forall x \in U)[(\exists y \in V)\pi(x, y) \Rightarrow (\exists y \in V)\rho(x, y)].$$

Now

$$\{x \in U : (\exists y \in V)\pi(x, y)\} = \text{Dom } \pi$$

and

$$\{x \in U : (\exists y \in V)\rho(x, y)\} = \text{Dom } \rho,$$

so the tautology just asserts

$$(\text{Dom } \pi) \subseteq (\text{Dom } \rho) \quad \text{if} \quad (\text{Ext } \pi) \subseteq (\text{Ext } \rho).$$

We draw a picture:

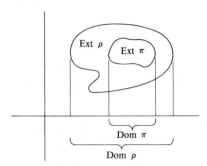

If one region is a subset of another, its projection on a line is a subset of the projection of the other on the same line. Small wonder, then, that Aristotle missed this one.

EXERCISES

In Exercises 1 through 7, derive the tautologies.

1. $(\forall x)(\exists y)[\pi(x, y) \wedge \sigma(x, y)] \wedge (\forall x)(\forall y)[\pi(x, y) \Rightarrow \rho(x, y)]$
   $\Rightarrow (\forall x)(\exists y)[\rho(x, y) \wedge \sigma(x, y)].$

2. $(\forall x)(\forall y)[\pi(x, y) \Rightarrow \rho(x, y)] \wedge (\exists x)(\forall y)[\sigma(x, y) \Rightarrow \pi(x, y)]$
   $\Rightarrow (\exists x)(\forall y)[\sigma(x, y) \Rightarrow \rho(x, y)].$

3. $(\forall x)(\exists y)[\pi(x, y) \wedge \sigma(x, y)] \wedge (\exists x)(\forall y)[\pi(x, y) \Rightarrow \rho(x, y)]$
   $\Rightarrow (\exists x)(\exists y)[\rho(x, y) \wedge \sigma(x, y)].$

4. $(\forall x)(\forall y)[\pi(x, y) \Rightarrow \rho(x, y)] \wedge (\forall x)(\forall y)[\sigma(x, y) \Rightarrow \tau(x, y)]$
   $\Rightarrow (\forall x)(\forall y)[\pi(x, y) \wedge \sigma(x, y) \Rightarrow \rho(x, y) \wedge \tau(x, y)].$

5. $(\forall x)(\forall y)[\pi(x, y) \Rightarrow \rho(x, y)] \wedge (\forall x)(\forall y)[\sigma(x, y) \Rightarrow \tau(x, y)]$
   $\Rightarrow \{(\forall x)(\exists y)[\pi(x, y) \wedge \sigma(x, y)] \Rightarrow (\forall x)(\exists y)[\rho(x, y) \wedge \tau(x, y)]\}.$

6. $(\forall x)(\forall y)[\pi(x, y) \Rightarrow \rho(x, y)] \wedge (\forall x)(\forall y)[\sigma(x, y) \Rightarrow \tau(x, y)]$
   $\wedge (\forall x)(\exists y)[\pi(x, y) \wedge \sigma(x, y)]$
   $\Rightarrow (\forall x)(\exists y)[\rho(x, y) \wedge \tau(x, y)].$

7. $(\forall x)[(\forall y)\pi(x, y) \Rightarrow (\forall z)\rho(x, z)] \wedge (\forall z)[(\forall y)\sigma(y, z) \Rightarrow (\forall x)\tau(x, z)]$
   $\Rightarrow (\forall x)(\forall z)\{(\forall y)[\pi(x, y) \wedge \sigma(y, z)] \Rightarrow [\rho(x, z) \wedge \tau(x, z)]\}.$

In Exercises 8 through 16, justify the inferences.

8. Some people can't stand anybody who is interested in sin.
   Everybody is interested in sin.
   ∴ Some people can't stand anybody (including themselves).

9. Some audiences like every ballet.
   No audience likes anything dull.
   ∴ No ballet is dull.

10. Every politician wants to be President.
    Some voters don't trust anybody who wants to be President.
    ∴ Some voters don't trust any politicians.

11. Some students like every course they understand.
    Every student dislikes at least one of the courses he passes.
    ∴ Some students pass some courses they don't understand.

12. Any mermaid can be found near some tropical island, but no mermaid can be found near any iceberg.
    ∴ If there are any mermaids, some tropical islands are not icebergs.

13. All bus drivers like all big trucks.
    No bus driver likes any Alfa.
    ∴ No Alfa is a big truck.

14. Somebody fights for everything he endorses.
    Everyone believes something he doesn't understand.
    Everyone endorses everything he believes.
    ∴ Somebody fights for something he doesn't understand.

15. Nobody should waste good money on any book that is just plain bad.
    Some people never read any books they don't really enjoy.
    Everybody reads some books that are just plain bad.
    ∴ Some people really enjoy some books on which they shouldn't waste good money.

16. No one approves of anything he feels is vulgar.
    Some people feel that anything they don't actually enjoy doing is vulgar.
    Everyone approves of something he wishes didn't have to be done at all.
    ∴ Someone actually enjoys doing something he wishes didn't have to be done at all.

CHAPTER FOUR

NUMBER SYSTEMS

In this chapter we examine the number systems of elementary mathematics in order to provide applications for some of the logical techniques we have considered in the previous chapters.

Before we can describe any number systems we must first discuss *functions* and *operations*. In Chapter 3 a binary relation was described as a two-place predicate, or as a condition whose extension is a subset of the cartesian product of a pair of sets. We define a *function* to be a special kind of binary relation: one whose extension contains, for each element of its domain, exactly one couple having that element as first component. In geometrical terms, a function is a relation whose graph does not contain a pair of dots one of which is directly above the other. With each element a of its domain a function f associates a unique element $f(a)$ of its range; $f(a)$ is usually called the *value of the function at a*. It is also customary to refer to a function as a *correspondence* or *mapping* from its domain to its range since, with each member of the former it associates precisely one member of the latter.

We may regard a condition on a universe as a function whose domain is the universe and whose range is a certain set of statements—but we could not take this as a definition of *condition* without closing a circle of definitions: a condition is a special kind of function, a function is a special kind of relation, and a relation is a special kind of condition. At least one of these terms must be left undefined—any reader who wishes to make his own choice is welcome to do so.

A (*binary*) *operation* is another kind of function: one whose domain is a product $U \times U$ and whose range is a subset of U. Such an operation is said to be *defined* on U. Examples familiar to school children are addition and multiplication of numbers: to each pair (a, b) of numbers another number $a + b$ is assigned by the operation addition—and similarly for multiplication, for which we write a dot instead of the plus sign.

1. ADDITION, MULTIPLICATION AND EQUALITY

In this section and the next we consider some mathematical proofs as examples to illustrate the theory of inference we have constructed. For these examples we select a fragment of the elementary theory of number systems. One reason for choosing number systems is their importance (one must know at least something about them for any study of mathematics). Another reason is that the proofs—while they may not be the most sophisticated of mathematical arguments—are intricate enough to provide reasonably interesting examples of inference problems.

We consider the five *elementary number systems*: the natural number system, the integers, the rational number system, the real number system, and the complex number system. For convenience we include zero in the set of natural numbers. Thus, in what follows, *natural number* is to be taken as a synonym for *nonnegative integer*. In some other books, but not in all, zero is excluded: in them, *natural number* corresponds to *positive integer*.

There is a good deal of similarity between the five systems and there are some important differences. Here we examine some of the similarities and a few of the differences.

In each case there is a set S, whose members are the numbers of the system, in each system there are binary operations called *addition* and *multiplication*, there is a binary relation called *equality*, and there are a number of properties of addition, multiplication and equality which are common to all five systems.

Binary relation on S is just another name for what we have called a *(binary) relation on $S \times S$*. The open sentence for the equality relation on S is written

$$x = y;$$

its extension is the set of all pairs in $S \times S$ whose first and second components are the "same."

Some of the properties of $=$, $+$, $\cdot$ common to all five of the number systems are these:

Equality is

Reflexive	$(\forall x \in S)[x = x]$,
Symmetric	$(\forall x \in S)(\forall y \in S)[(x = y) \Rightarrow (y = x)]$,
Transitive	$(\forall x)(\forall y)(\forall z)[(x = y) \wedge (y = z) \Rightarrow (x = z)]$,

and is "preserved by the operations"

$$(\forall x)(\forall y)(\forall z)[(x = y) \Rightarrow (x + z = y + z)],$$
$$(\forall x)(\forall y)(\forall z)[(x = y) \Rightarrow (x \cdot z = y \cdot z)].$$

Addition is

Commutative $(\forall x)(\forall y)[x + y = y + x],$

Associative $(\forall x)(\forall y)(\forall z)[x + (y + z) = (x + y) + z],$

and has an

Identity $(\exists v \in S)(\forall x \in S)[v + x = x].$

Multiplication is

Commutative $(\forall x)(\forall y)[x \cdot y = y \cdot x],$

Associative $(\forall x)(\forall y)(\forall z)[x \cdot (y \cdot z) = (x \cdot y) \cdot z)],$

and has an

Identity $(\exists u \in S)(\forall x \in S)[u \cdot x = x].$

Distributivity $(\forall x)(\forall y)(\forall z)[x \cdot (y + z) = xy + xz].$

Here, of course, is an example of mathematical abstraction. Note that the terms *addition*, *multiplication*, and *equality* have not been defined. All that has been claimed about them is that the first two name binary operations and the third a binary relation which have all the properties listed. Because the properties in the list are shared by many systems, including the five number systems, any conclusions one may draw from the list also represent properties common to all those systems. For instance, reading *union* and *intersection* for *addition* and *multiplication*, we have a list of some of the properties of Boolean algebras; thus even they are among the systems which provide "interpretations" of our list of properties.

As a convenient generic name for any system with all the properties listed above we shall use the term *semiring*. Thus the sentence *the integers form a semiring* is just a concise version of the assertion that the system of integers has all the properties listed. There are generic terms for some special kinds of semirings. Three we shall encounter, at least briefly, are *ring, integral domain, field*.

Given the list of defining properties for a semiring, we shall be interested in other properties of two kinds: properties which are consequences of those in the list, and properties which are not. Such of the former as we discuss will be identified by proving that they are consequences; the latter will be identified by citing counterexamples.

We turn now to some illustrations of the kind of proofs one encounters frequently in discussions of number systems.

We consider first the "identity" properties. One thing which distinguishes these two from all the other defining properties of a semiring is the presence of existential quantifiers. Thus, if only because it must have an identity for each operation, no semiring can be void. The identity properties, by themselves, require only that each operation have at least one identity. However, using these properties along with some of the others, we can prove that neither operation in a semiring may have more than one identity. A member of S is an identity for addition if it satisfies the condition

$$(\forall x \in S)[u + x = x]$$

on the variable u. We are to prove that the extension of this condition is a singleton:

$$(\forall u)(\forall v)\{(\forall x)(u + x = x) \land (\forall x)(v + x = x) \Rightarrow (u = v)\}.$$

And similarly, with $\cdot$ in place of $+$.

Theorem 1 The identities of a semiring are unique.

Proof. Consider addition. If u and v are identities, then

$$v + u = u \quad \text{and} \quad u + v = v.$$

But equality is symmetric,

$$u = v + u \quad \text{and} \quad u + v = v;$$

the operation is commutative,

$$u = v + u, \quad v + u = u + v, \quad \text{and} \quad u + v = v;$$

and equality is transitive,

$$u = v.$$

For multiplication, we need merely write $\cdot$ in place of $+$.

Now that we know there cannot be more than one identity for addition or more than one for multiplication, we are entitled to assign them names: write 0 for *the* additive identity and 1 for *the* multiplicative identity. Using these names we rewrite the identity properties in the forms we shall cite from now on:

$$(\forall x \in S)[0 + x = x], \qquad (\forall x \in S)[1 \cdot x = x].$$

Next we add another property to the list and concentrate on a special type of semiring (the five number systems are still included as examples, but most Boolean algebras are not).

Cancellation for Addition

$$(\forall x \in S)(\forall y \in S)(\forall z \in S)[(x + z = y + z) \Rightarrow (x = y)].$$

Note that this cancellation property is a converse of the additive property of equality. Note also that a Boolean algebra has this property only if it has just one member (Exercise 2, page 72). Our main theorem on semirings with additive cancellation is the following one.

Theorem 2 If S is a semiring with cancellation for addition, then

$$(\forall x \in S)[x \cdot 0 = 0].$$

Proof. Since 0 is the additive identity,

$$0 + 1 = 1.$$

Then, by the multiplicative property of equality, for any x in S,

$$x(0 + 1) = x \cdot 1.$$

Using the distributive law and the fact that 1 is the multiplicative identity, we have

$$x(0 + 1) = x \cdot 0 + x \cdot 1 = x \cdot 0 + x \quad \text{and} \quad x \cdot 1 = x.$$

But 0 is the additive identity, so

$$x \cdot 0 + x = x = 0 + x.$$

Canceling the second terms on right and left:

$$x \cdot 0 = 0.$$

We have seen that the identities are unique; we now consider whether or not they are distinct. We mentioned one example of a semiring with additive cancellation in which they are equal; it is easy to see that there are no others.

Corollary If S is a semiring with additive cancellation and 0, 1 are its identities, then

$$0 = 1 \quad \text{if and only if} \quad (\forall x \in S)[x = 0].$$

Proof. Suppose $0 = 1$. Then, for any x in S,

$$x = 1 \cdot x = x \cdot 1 = x \cdot 0 = 0.$$

The converse is even easier: If every member of S is 0, then 1, being a member of S, is too.

Definition A semiring with just one member will be called a *trivial* semiring.

Digression We interrupt our series of proofs for some comments on those we have already.

In writing the proofs we have included about as many quantifiers as one is likely to find in any piece of mathematical writing outside of logic books. Such stinginess with quantifiers can be rationalized as follows: With one exception (cf.

Exercise 6, page 145), each of the steps in these arguments has the form

$$(\forall x)\alpha(x)$$
$$\therefore (\forall x)\beta(x)$$

and is justified by an appeal to

$$(\forall x)[\alpha(x) \Rightarrow \beta(x)]$$

as a premise, although the quantifiers are left unwritten and the authority is cited only by name. One of our change-of-scope tautologies lets us infer

$$(\forall x)\alpha(x) \Rightarrow (\forall x)\beta(x)$$

from the authority we cite while this, along with $(\forall x)\alpha(x)$, yields $(\forall x)\beta(x)$. Thus, except for the missing quantifiers, what is left out is an easily justified logical step which may be considered too trivial to mention.

The missing quantifiers are accounted for by blanket phrases like *for any x, for arbitrary x*, etc., often put near the front of the proof [Theorem 2 and Corollary], or simply left for the reader to supply [Theorem 1]. We can justify using just one universal quantifier to serve for each line of the proof by appealing to the tautology

$$(\forall x)[\pi(x) \wedge \rho(x)] \Leftrightarrow [(\forall x)\pi(x)] \wedge [(\forall x)\rho(x)],$$

if we interpret the blanket quantifier as applied to the conjunction of all the lines of the proof. Compare, in particular, the proof of the corollary: here

$$x = 1 \cdot x = x \cdot 1 = x \cdot 0 = 0$$

is in fact just the conjunction of

$$x = 1 \cdot x, \quad 1 \cdot x = x \cdot 1, \quad x \cdot 1 = x \cdot 0, \quad \text{and} \quad x \cdot 0 = 0.$$

More care would be required, of course, if existential quantifiers were involved. But so far we have managed to avoid them.

Rings

A pair of elements of a semiring whose sum is the additive identity are called *additive inverses* of each other.

A condition on semirings even stronger than additive cancellation is the requirement that each member have an additive inverse.

Additive Inverse $(\forall x \in S)(\exists y \in S)[x + y = 0]$.

We shall see that a semiring with the additive inverse property is automatically a semiring with cancellation for addition. That the inverse condition is actually stronger than the cancellation condition is illustrated by the fact that the natural number system, which does have the cancellation property, does not have the inverse property. The other four number systems have both properties.

A semiring with the additive inverse property will be called a *ring* in what follows. There is not much agreement on this terminology. Very few writers require that a ring have a multiplicative identity, most do not require commutativity for multiplication, and many do not even require associativity for multiplication. Thus, in some circles, what we call a *ring* is known as a *commutative associative ring with identity*.

First we prove that no member of any semiring can have more than one additive inverse.

Theorem 3

$$(\forall x \in S)(\forall y \in S)(\forall z \in S)\{(x + y = 0) \wedge (x + z = 0) \Rightarrow (y = z)\}.$$

Proof

$$y = y + 0 = y + (x + z) = (y + x) + z = (x + y) + z = 0 + z = z.$$

(Note that, because none of the properties of multiplication are invoked, this proof can be used for any ring, no matter which of the current definitions one may adopt.)

Thus a ring is a semiring in which each element has one and only one additive inverse. If R is a ring and $a \in R$, it is customary to write $-a$ for the unique additive inverse of a, and to define on R a new operation, called *subtraction*, by writing

$$a - b = a + (-b).$$

With these definitions one can deduce a number of results of the following kind:

$$(-a)b = -(ab), \qquad (-a)(-b) = ab, \qquad a(b - c) = (ab) - (ac).$$

We leave these as exercises and turn, instead, to the question of cancellation.

Theorem 4 In any ring the cancellation law for addition holds.

Proof. The argument is often presented as follows: Suppose

$$x + z = y + z.$$

Add $-z$ to each side,

$$(x + z) + (-z) = (y + z) + (-z),$$

use associativity,

$$x + (z + (-z)) = y + (z + (-z)),$$

the definition of inverse,

$$x + 0 = y + 0,$$

and the identity property,

$$x = y.$$

Corollary In any ring, $(\forall x)[x \cdot 0 = 0]$.

A more "formal" version of the proof given above for Theorem 4 runs as follows. To prove, using the properties of a semiring,

$$(\forall z)(\exists u)(z + u = 0) \Rightarrow (\forall x)(\forall y)(\forall z)[(x + z = y + z) \Rightarrow (x = y)]$$

or, equivalently (Exercise 1, page 113),

$$(\forall x)(\forall y)\{(\forall z)(\exists u)(z + u = 0) \Rightarrow (\forall z)[(x + z = y + z) \Rightarrow (x = y)]\}.$$

But the latter follows (C1) from

$$(\forall x)(\forall y)(\forall z)\{(\exists u)(z + u = 0) \Rightarrow [(x + z = y + z) \Rightarrow (x = y)]\},$$

which, in turn, amounts to (Exercise 1, page 113)

$$(\forall x)(\forall y)(\forall z)(\forall u)\{(z + u = 0) \Rightarrow [(x + z = y + z) \Rightarrow (x = y)]\}$$

or (Exercise 2, page 107)

$$(\forall x)(\forall y)(\forall z)(\forall u)\{[(z + u = 0) \wedge (x + z = y + z)] \Rightarrow (x = y)\}.$$

So, again, we have only universal quantifiers to work with. What is left is essentially the sorites that we wrote down originally:

$$x + z = y + z \Rightarrow (x + z) + u = (y + z) + u$$
$$\Rightarrow x + (z + u) = y + (z + u),$$

so

$$(x + z = y + z) \wedge (z + u = 0) \Rightarrow x + 0 = y + 0$$
$$\Rightarrow x = y.$$

Integral Domains and Fields

We next consider cancellation for multiplication and the existence of multiplicative inverses.

Because $(\forall x)[x \cdot 0 = 0]$ for any semiring with additive cancellation it is necessary to place a restriction on the cancellation of factors common to each side of an equality. Indeed, for such a semiring, we have

$$(\forall x)(\forall y)[x \cdot 0 = y \cdot 0];$$

but

$$(\forall x)(\forall y)[x = y]$$

is just another version of the assertion that the semiring be trivial. Hence the factor 0 can be canceled only in the trivial semiring. However, in each of the number systems any nonzero factor may be canceled.

Writing S^* for the set of nonzero members of a semiring S, we formulate our multiplicative cancellation property as follows.

Cancellation for Multiplication

$$(\forall x \in S)(\forall y \in S)(\forall z \in S^*)[(xz = yz) \Rightarrow (x = y)].$$

Each of the five number systems is a semiring having both cancellation properties. (A Boolean algebra with more than one member is a semiring with neither of the cancellation properties.) A nontrivial ring with cancellation for multiplication is called an *integral domain*. Apparently there are no special names for semirings with both of the cancellation properties, although such systems have some interesting properties. For example, in a semiring with additive cancellation a product ab is 0 if either a or b is 0 [Theorem 2]; the converse holds in a semiring with both of the cancellation properties.

Theorem 5 If S is a semiring with both additive and multiplicative cancellation, then

$$(\forall x \in S)(\forall y \in S)\{(xy = 0) \Rightarrow [(x = 0) \vee (y = 0)]\}.$$

Proof. Suppose $xy = 0$ and $y \neq 0$. By Theorem 2, $xy = 0y$; and, since $y \neq 0$, y may be canceled. Thus $x = 0$.

Moreover, in a ring the requirement that a product be zero only if at least one of the factors is zero is enough to guarantee cancellation for multiplication. Thus, at least in the ring case, the two requirements are equivalent.

Theorem 6 If R is a ring and if

$$(\forall x \in R)(\forall y \in R)\{(xy = 0) \Rightarrow [(x = 0) \vee (y = 0)]\},$$

then R is a ring with cancellation for multiplication.

Proof. If $xz = yz$, then $xz - yz = 0$ and $(x - y)z = 0$. Hence $x - y = 0$ or $z = 0$; that is,

$$xz = yz \quad \text{and} \quad z \neq 0 \quad \text{imply} \quad x = y.$$

When we come to multiplicative inverses we encounter the same problem we did with multiplicative cancellation. A pair of elements of a semiring are *multiplicative inverses* (or *reciprocals*) of each other if their product is the multiplicative identity. Clearly 0 can have a multiplicative inverse in a semiring with additive cancellation, only if the semiring is trivial: there is an a for which

$$0 \cdot a = 1$$

only if $1 = 0$, since $0 \cdot a = 0$. Indeed, if $1 = 0$, then 0 is its own inverse: $0 \cdot 0 = 0 = 1$. (Hence the conclusion that there is only one "number system" available to all who would "divide by zero"—and the corollary that it is the one that should be used for reckoning their grades.)

The last property we mention here is this:

Multiplicative Inverse $(\forall x \in S^*)(\exists y \in S^*)[xy = 1]$.

A nontrivial ring with this property is called a *field*. (Or a *division ring* if commutativity for multiplication is not required.)

Theorem 7 No member of a semiring may have more than one reciprocal.

Proof. Rewrite the proof of Theorem 3, putting $\cdot$ and 1 in place of $+$ and 0, respectively.

Theorem 8 A field is an integral domain.

Proof. Rewrite the proof of Theorem 4, putting $(\forall z \in S^*)$, $(\exists u \in S^*)$, $(\forall u \in S^*)$, $\cdot$, and 1 in place of $(\forall z \in S)$, $(\exists u \in S)$, $(\forall u \in S)$, $+$, and 0, respectively.

Corollary In any field

$$xy = 0 \qquad \text{if and only if} \qquad x = 0 \quad \text{or} \quad y = 0.$$

EXERCISES

1. Suppose $*$ is a commutative binary operation on a set S:

$$(\forall x)(\forall y)[x * y = y * x].$$

If $n \in S$ and $(\forall x \in S)[n * x = n]$, call n a *null* (for $*$). [Thus, according to Theorem 2, 0 is a null (for $\cdot$) in a semiring with additive cancellation.] Show that S cannot have more than one null for any commutative operation $*$ defined on S.

2. If the distributive property is dropped and replaced by the "absorption laws"

$$(\forall x)(\forall y)[x = x + xy], \qquad (\forall x)(\forall y)[x = x(x + y)],$$

the resulting system is called a *lattice* (with identities), rather than a semiring. Prove that in such a lattice, the identity for each operation is a null for the other operation:

$$(\forall x)[x \cdot 0 = 0], \qquad (\forall x)[x + 1 = 1].$$

[Thus, the result in Theorem 2 holds in any Boolean algebra (which is both a lattice and a semiring), although neither cancellation law holds if there is more than one element.]

3. In any ring both $1 + (-1) = 0$ and $(-1) + 1 = 0$, and since each member of a ring has a unique additive inverse, it follows from the second of these equalities that the second term is the inverse of the first term: $1 = -(-1)$. Prove that the equality $(-1)[1 + (-1)] = (-1)0$ leads to the conclusion $(-1)(-1) = -(-1)$ and, hence, using the previous result, $(-1)(-1) = 1$.

4. By an argument similar to that in Exercise 3, prove that in a ring, $-x = (-1)x$, for each x.

5. From the results in Exercises 3 and 4 deduce: For each x, y, z,

$$-(-x) = x, \qquad (-x)y = -(xy), \qquad (-x)(-y) = xy,$$
$$x(y - z) = (xy) - (xz).$$

6. (a) A formal proof for Theorem 1,

$$(\forall u)(\forall v)[(\forall x)(u + x = x) \wedge (\forall x)(v + x = x) \Rightarrow (u = v)],$$

may be constructed in two steps by proving

$$(\forall u)(\forall v)[(\forall x)(u + x = x) \wedge (\forall x)(v + x = x)$$
$$\Rightarrow (u + v = v) \wedge (v + u = u)],$$
$$(\forall u)(\forall v)[(u + v = v) \wedge (v + u = u) \Rightarrow (u = v)].$$

Write a formal proof for the second step (the argument sketched informally in the text).

(b) To complete the proof of Theorem 1, use Exercise 6, page 128, to prove

$$(\forall u)[(\forall x)(u + x = x) \Rightarrow (\forall v)(u + v = v)],$$
$$(\forall v)[(\forall x)(v + x = x) \Rightarrow (\forall u)(v + u = u)],$$

and then use the tautology in Exercise 7, page 133.

2. ORDER RELATIONS AND INEQUALITIES

In this section we study inequalities in the elementary number systems. We first consider order relations in general and then concentrate on the special case of semirings, where the connection between the algebraic operations and the order relation is very important. We divide the discussion of semirings into two parts: first we consider a special case involving semirings which are not rings, and then we extend the results to the case of rings. We close this section with a comparative study of the order properties of the various number systems.

If S is a set, a binary relation $\leq$ defined on S is called a *partial order relation* provided it has the following three properties:

For each x, y, z in S,

(1) $x = y$ implies $x \leq y$,

(2) $x \leq y$ and $y \leq z$ imply $x \leq z$,

(3) $x \leq y$ and $y \leq x$ imply $x = y$.

These properties are called, respectively, *reflexivity*, *transitivity*, and *antisymmetry*. If a partial order relation is defined on S, S is called a *partially ordered set*. A partial order relation is called a *chain ordering* or a *linear ordering* provided it has the following additional property:

For each x, y in S,

(4) either $x \leq y$ or $y \leq x$.

In this case the set is called a *chain*.

For example, set inclusion is a partial ordering which (except in the case of a two-element Boolean algebra) is not a chain ordering. The relations "less than or equal," which will be defined below for the natural numbers, integers, rationals, and real numbers, are all chain orderings.

Given a set S and a partial ordering $\leq$ defined on S, we may introduce another relation $<$ with the following definition:

For each x, y in S,

(5) $x < y$ if and only if $x \leq y$ and $x \neq y$.

Theorem 1 If $\leq$ is a partial order relation on S and if $<$ is defined by (5), then, for each x, y, z in S,

(6) $x \leq y$ if and only if $x < y$ or $x = y$,

(7) $x < y$ and $y < z$ imply $x < z$,

(8) $x \leq y$ implies $y \not< x$.

Proof. From (5),

$$(x \not< y) \Rightarrow [(x \leq y) \Rightarrow (x = y)];$$

so

$$(x \leq y) \Rightarrow [(x \not< y) \Rightarrow (x = y)]   \qquad \text{[E-6, page 25}$$

or

$$(x \leq y) \Rightarrow (x < y) \vee (x = y).$$

But (5) also gives

$$(x < y) \Rightarrow (x \leq y),$$

which, with (1), yields

$$(x < y) \vee (x = y) \Rightarrow (x \leq y).   \qquad \text{[E-11, page 25}$$

Hence

$$(x \leq y) \Leftrightarrow (x < y) \vee (x = y),$$

which is (6). For (7), we first prove

(9) $(x < y) \wedge (y < z) \Rightarrow (x \neq z)$.

Assume that $x < y$, $y < z$, $x = z$; then [cf. Exercise 1, below] $x < y$ and $y < x$; so, from (5), $x \leq y$ and $y \leq x$ but $x \neq y$, contradicting (3). From (5) we also get

$$(x < y) \wedge (y < z) \Rightarrow (x \leq y) \wedge (y \leq z),$$

which, with (2), gives

$$(x < y) \wedge (y < z) \Rightarrow (x \leq z),$$

and, using (9), we derive (7):

$$(x < y) \wedge (y < z) \Rightarrow (x < z).   \qquad \text{[E-8, page 25}$$

To prove (8) assume the contrary:

$$x \leq y \quad \text{and} \quad y < x.$$

Using (5), we infer

$$x \leq y, \quad y \leq x, \quad \text{and} \quad x \neq y,$$

contradicting (3). The proof is complete.

    In view of (5) and (6), $<$ and $\leq$ may be read "less than" and "less than or equal to," respectively. According to (7), $<$ is a transitive relation; one consequence of (8) is that $<$ is *irreflexive*:

For each x, y in S,

(10) $x = y$ implies $x \not< y$.

Indeed, if we use (6), we can rewrite (8) as follows:

$$(x < y) \lor (x = y) \Rightarrow (y \not< x);$$

so

$$(x = y) \Rightarrow (y \not< x). \qquad \text{[T-7, page 25}$$

Moreover, the converse of (8) is equivalent to (4), the condition that S be a chain.

Theorem 2 If $\leq$ is a chain ordering of S, then, for each x, y in S,

(11) $x \leq y$ if and only if $y \not< x$.

Proof. Using (6), we can rewrite (4) in the following forms:

$$x \leq y, \quad \text{or} \quad x = y, \quad \text{or} \quad y < x,$$
$$x \leq y \quad \text{or} \quad y < x,$$

that is,

$$y \not< x \quad \text{implies} \quad x \leq y,$$

which is just the converse of (8). Q.E.D.

    Properties (5), (6), and (11) together give the so-called *trichotomy* property:

(12) For each pair x, y in S, exactly one of the following three relations holds:

$$x < y, \quad x = y, \quad y < x.$$

With (6), the "if" part of (11) is the assertion that at least one of the three relations holds:

$$(x < y) \lor (x = y) \lor (y < x).$$

To prove that at most one of them holds, observe that (5) and the "only if" part of (11) give

$$(x < y) \Rightarrow (x \neq y), \quad (x < y) \Rightarrow (y \not< x), \quad (x = y) \Rightarrow (y \not< x),$$

which rule out, respectively,

$x < y$ and $x = y$, $x < y$ and $y < x$, $x = y$ and $y < x$.

It is customary to define $x \geq y$ and $x > y$ to mean $y \leq x$ and $y < x$, respectively; but it is never really necessary to use either of these relations.

EXERCISE

1. Suppose $\leq$ is defined on S and has properties (1), (2), (5), and (6). Prove that for each x, y, z in S,
   (a) $(x = y) \Rightarrow [(z \leq x) \Rightarrow (z \leq y)]$,
   (b) $(x = y) \Rightarrow [(x \leq z) \Rightarrow (y \leq z)]$,
   (c) $(x = y) \Rightarrow [(z < x) \Rightarrow (z < y)]$,
   (d) $(x = y) \Rightarrow [(x < z) \Rightarrow (y < z)]$.

Ordered Semirings

We now consider inequalities in number systems, and investigate the relationship between arithmetical operations and order relations defined on semirings.

A Boolean algebra is a semiring (if $+$ and $\cdot$ are union and intersection), partially ordered by inclusion, with both of the following properties:

For each x, y, z,

(13) $x \leq y$ implies $x + z \leq y + z$,

(14) $x \leq y$ implies $xz \leq yz$.

("Addition and multiplication *preserve* the order relation.") We shall find that in certain semirings which are not rings, it is possible to define chain orderings which have both of these properties. However, in a ring with more than one element, it is impossible to define a chain ordering having both properties. Indeed, for a chain ordering, either $0 \leq 1$ or $1 \leq 0$. If $0 \leq 1$, add -1 to each side: $-1 \leq 0$. Then multiply each side by -1: $1 \leq 0$. But if $1 \leq 0$, first add -1, $0 \leq -1$; then multiply by -1, $0 \leq 1$. So, in either case, both $0 \leq 1$ and $1 \leq 0$, that is, $0 = 1$.

In any semiring, $0 + 0 = 0$. In some semirings, but not in all, the following condition holds:

(15) $x + y = 0$ if and only if $x = 0$ and $y = 0$.

We invent the term *natural domain* for a semiring with this property. Some examples of natural domains are the semiring of natural numbers, Boolean algebras ($A \cup B = \emptyset$ if and only if $A = \emptyset$ and $B = \emptyset$), the semiring of the nonnegative rationals, and the semiring of the nonnegative reals. No ring with more than one element is a natural domain.

In any semiring S we can define a relation $\leq$ as follows:

(16) For each x, y in S, $x \leq y$ if and only if there is a z in S such that

$$x + z = y.$$

Theorem 3 If S is a semiring, the relation defined in (16) is reflexive and transitive and is preserved by both addition and multiplication. If S is a natural domain with cancellation for addition, the relation defined in (16) is antisymmetric.

Proof. Reflexivity follows from the fact that $x + 0 = x$, for each x. For transitivity, suppose $x \leq y$ and $y \leq z$. Then there are u, v in S for which

$$x + u = y \quad \text{and} \quad y + v = z.$$

Hence

$$x + (u + v) = z,$$

where $u + v \in S$; so $x \leq z$. For the preservation by addition and multiplication, suppose $x \leq y$. Then $x + u = y$, for some u, so

$$(x + z) + u = y + z \quad \text{and} \quad xz + uz = yz,$$

where both u and uz are in S. That is,

$$x + z \leq y + z \quad \text{and} \quad xz \leq yz.$$

For the antisymmetry, suppose $x \leq y$ and $y \leq x$. Then there are u, v in S satisfying

$$x + u = y \quad \text{and} \quad y + v = x.$$

So

$$x + (u + v) = (x + u) + v = y + v = x,$$
$$x + (u + v) = x + 0,$$

and, canceling x,

$$u + v = 0.$$

But, then, $u = v = 0$, and $x = y$.

In the semiring of natural numbers, as well as in the semirings of non-negative rationals and nonnegative reals, the relation (16) is a chain ordering, for reasons we shall encounter later. The assertion that (16) defines a chain ordering is, of course, a statement about the "solvability" of certain pairs of equations:

For each x, y in S, either there is a u for which $x + u = y$, or there is a v for which $x = y + v$.

EXERCISES

1. Suppose that S is a semiring with cancellation for addition and that $\leq$ is a partial order relation on S satisfying (13); prove that the relation $<$ defined in (5) has the following property: For each x, y, z,

   (13*) $x < y$ implies $x + z < y + z$.

2. Prove (as a kind of converse of the previous result) that if S is a semiring partially ordered by $\leq$ and if the relation $<$ defined in (5) has property (13*), then the cancellation law for addition holds in S if S is a chain. [*Hint:* Use the trichotomy property.]

Ordered Rings

We have seen that in a ring with more than one element, no relation can have all of the properties (1), (2), (3), (4), (13), (14). As a matter of fact, in any ring in which there is a relation satisfying only (3), (4) and (14), we must have $1 + 1 = 0$. [Either $-1 \leq 1$ or $1 \leq -1$. Multiply by -1: then $1 \leq -1$ or $-1 \leq 1$, respectively. So, in each case, both $1 \leq -1$ and $-1 \leq 1$. Hence $1 = -1$ and $1 + 1 = 0$.] There can be no hope, then, of defining a chain order for integers, rational, or real numbers, unless we dispense with property (14). The question remains whether we can satisfy all the other requirements even if we do omit (14), or if we modify it in some way.

We examine the proof of Theorem 3 to see what modifications might be made that would enable us to carry through as much of the argument as possible under the assumption that S is a ring. In the first place definition (16) itself must be changed: If S is a ring, then for each x, y in S, there is a z in S which satisfies $x + z = y$; namely $z = y - x$. We would like, of course, to change the definition as little as possible. Although we might presumably change any of the three quantifiers, if the domain and the range of the relation are to remain all of S, we must leave those on x and y as they are, and if not every member of S is to be less than or equal to every member of S, we will have to change the quantifier on z. Suppose we consider restricting the quantifier on z to some proper subset A of S, and try to find out what properties A must have if we are to reconstruct a proof for the theorem.

To make our proof go through for the transitivity of the relation, we shall assume that the sum of each pair of members of A is also a member of A. Observe, indeed, that the inequality relation will also be preserved under multiplication if we restrict the multipliers to be members of A and require that A contain the product of each pair of its members. For reflexivity, we require $0 \in A$. Thus, except for the possibility that 1 might not need to be a member of A, we conclude that the set A should not only be a proper subset of the ring, but that it should, in fact, be a semiring in its own right. To make the antisymmetry argument go through, we will still assume that A is a natural domain. (Since A is a subset of a ring, cancellation for addition holds automatically.)

Suppose, then, that R is a ring and that A is a proper subset of R which contains 0 as well as the sum and product of each pair of members of A. Define

(17) For each x, y in R, $x \leq y$ if and only if there is a z in A for which

$$x + z = y.$$

Then we have the following theorem.

Theorem 4 If R is a ring and A is a proper subset of R which is also a natural domain, the relation defined in (17) is reflexive, transitive, anti-symmetric, preserved by addition, and has the following property:

(18) For each x, y in R and each z in A,

$$x \leq y \quad \text{implies} \quad xz \leq yz.$$

Observe that the members of A are all greater than or equal to zero, and that no other members of R are greater than or equal to zero: restricting the quantifier on x in (17) to the set $\{0\}$ gives

For each y in R, $0 \leq y$ if and only if there is a z in A for which $0 + z = y$.

Observe also that an element of R is less than or equal to zero only if its additive inverse is a member of A: put $y = 0$ and take $z = -x$ in (13), then for each x in R,

$$x \leq 0 \quad \text{implies} \quad 0 \leq -x.$$

Thus the condition

(19) For each x in R,

$$\text{either} \quad x \in A \quad \text{or} \quad -x \in A$$

is a necessary condition for the order relation defined by (17) to be a chain ordering of R. But this condition is also sufficient to assure that the ordering be a chain ordering; for if $z = y - x$, then

$$z \in A \quad \text{if and only if} \quad x \leq y,$$

and

$$-z \in A \quad \text{if and only if} \quad y \leq x;$$

so condition (19) implies

$$\text{either} \quad x \leq y \quad \text{or} \quad y \leq x.$$

for each x and y in R.

Write $\overline{A}$ for the set of the additive inverses of the members of A. Then condition (19) for a chain ordering can be expressed as follows:

$$R = A \cup \overline{A}.$$

In this notation, the condition

$$A \cap \overline{A} = \{0\}$$

guarantees that the semiring A is a natural domain, and is, indeed, a necessary and sufficient condition that the relation (17) be antisymmetric. Here $A \cap \overline{A} = \{0\}$ if and only if 0 is the only member of A whose additive inverse is also a member of A, so $z \in A$ and $-z \in A$ if and only if $z = 0$; that is,

$$x \leq y \quad \text{and} \quad y \leq x \qquad \text{if and only if} \qquad x = y.$$

For a chain ordering we must have either $-1 \in A$, or $1 \in A$, but not both. However, if A is to contain all products of members of A, it must also contain the square of each of its members. So if -1 were a member of A, it would follow that its square must also be a member of A, which [since $(-1) + (-1)^2 = 0$] is contrary to our requirement that A be a natural domain. So, for a chain ordering, we must have $1 \in A$, and we cannot have $-1 \in A$.

In the complex number system there are two members, i and $-i$, whose squares are -1. If it were possible to find a natural domain A such that $A \cup \overline{A}$ were the whole complex number system, while $A \cap \overline{A} = \{0\}$, then either i or $-i$ would have to be a member of A. But both these alternatives are impossible, because in either case A would then contain both -1 and 1, the second and fourth powers of $\pm i$. We conclude then that (17) cannot be used to define a chain ordering of the complex numbers.

When it is possible to decompose a ring R as the union of subsets A, $\overline{A}$ with A a natural domain, $\overline{A}$ the set of the additive inverses of the members of A, and $A \cap \overline{A} = \{0\}$, it is customary to say that R is *ordered*, that the nonzero members of A are *positive*, and that the nonzero members of $\overline{A}$ are *negative*; in this case the order relation itself is defined by (17). In the ring I of integers, the semiring of nonnegative integers is the set N of natural numbers: each integer which is not a natural number is the additive inverse of a natural number. The rational and real fields are both ordered; in each case there is a subset of numbers which forms a natural domain, and all the other numbers are the additive inverses of the members of this subset. The complex field is not ordered, for, although it contains several natural domains (each of those mentioned above is one), it does not contain any so large that it, together with the set of its additive inverses, exhausts the entire complex field.

EXERCISES

In these Exercises, S is an ordered semiring with cancellation for addition (as in Exercise 1, page 150), R is an ordered ring with cancellation for multiplication, F is an ordered field, and $a < b < c$ is an abbreviation for $a < b$ *and* $b < c$. Prove each of the following assertions.

1. For each x, y, z, w in S,

$$x < y \quad \text{and} \quad z < w \quad \text{imply} \quad x + z < y + w.$$

2. For each x, y in R,

$$x \leq y \quad \text{if and only if} \quad -y \leq -x,$$
$$x < y \quad \text{if and only if} \quad -y < -x.$$

3. For each x, y, z in R,

$$x < y \quad \text{and} \quad 0 < z \quad \text{imply} \quad xz < yz,$$
$$x < y \quad \text{and} \quad z < 0 \quad \text{imply} \quad yz < xz.$$

4. For each x, y, z, w in R,

$$x < y \quad \text{and} \quad 0 < z < w \quad \text{imply} \quad xz < yw.$$

5. For each x in R,

$$0 < x < 1 \quad \text{implies} \quad 0 < x^2 < x < 1.$$

6. For each x, y in F,

$$x < 0 < y \quad \text{if and only if} \quad \frac{1}{x} < 0 < \frac{1}{y},$$

$$0 < x < y \quad \text{if and only if} \quad 0 < \frac{1}{y} < \frac{1}{x},$$

$$0 < \frac{x}{y} \quad \text{if and only if} \quad 0 < xy.$$

7. For each x, y, z, w in F, if $yw > 0$, then

$$\frac{x}{y} < \frac{z}{w} \quad \text{if and only if} \quad xw < yz.$$

Lower Bounds and Upper Bounds

If S is a partially ordered set and if T is a subset of S, an element a of S is called a *lower bound* of T provided

$$(\forall x \in T)(a \leq x),$$

and an element b of S is called an *upper bound* of T provided

$$(\forall x \in T)(x \leq b).$$

If a is a lower bound of T, every member of S less than a is also a lower bound of T; and if b is an upper bound of T, every member of S greater than b is also an upper bound of T.

A lower bound of T which is also a member of T is called a *least element*, or *least member*, of T; an upper bound of T which is also a member of T is called a *greatest element*, or *greatest member*, of T. Although a set may have neither a least member nor a greatest member, the antisymmetry of the order relation implies that no set can have more than one least member, or more than one greatest member.

A partial ordering defined on a set S is said to be a *well ordering* of S provided each nonvoid subset of S has a least member; the set S is said to be *well ordered* by such an order relation. Observe that a well-ordered set is necessarily a chain: for each pair a, b of members of S, one of the members of the nonvoid subset $\{a, b\}$ must be less than or equal to the other one.

If a and b are members of S, the set

$$\{x \in S : a < x < b\}$$

is called an *open interval* of S. If S is a chain, its order relation is said to be *discrete* if each nonvoid open interval of S has a least element and a greatest element. If S is a chain, its order relation is said to be *dense* if no open interval of S has either a least element or a greatest element.

In the semiring of the natural numbers the order relation (16) is a discrete well ordering.

In the ring of integers, the order relation (17) is discrete.

In the field of rational numbers, the order relation (17) is dense.

Suppose S is an ordered set and T is a subset of S. A least member of the set of all upper bounds of T is called a *supremum* of T. A greatest member of the set of all lower bounds of T is called an *infimum* of T. A set may have neither an infimum nor a supremum, but no set can have more than one of each. The order relation of S is said to be *complete* if each nonvoid subset of S which has an upper bound also has a supremum.

In the field of real numbers, the order relation (17) is complete.

EXERCISES

Prove each of the following assertions.

1. If T is a subset of S and a is a lower bound of T, then every member of S less than a is also a lower bound of T; and if b is an upper bound of T, every member of S greater than b is also an upper bound of T.

2. No set may have more than one least member or more than one greatest member, and no set may have more than one infimum or more than one supremum.

3. A chain ordering of S is dense if and only if there is at least one member of S between each pair of distinct members of S.

4. If R is an ordered ring and A is a subset of R that is bounded above (or bounded below), then B is bounded below (or bounded above, respectively), if B is the set of the additive inverses of the members of A.

5. If R is an ordered ring, its order relation is complete if each nonvoid subset of R which has a lower bound also has an infimum.

6. 1 is the smallest positive integer. [Assume that $\{x \in N : 0 < x < 1\}$ is non-void and use the fact that N is well ordered to conclude that this set has a least member. Show that this conclusion leads to a contradiction.] If n is a positive integer, then $n - 1$ is a natural number. [Use the previous result to conclude that $n \geq 1$.]

3. MATHEMATICAL INDUCTION

Mathematical induction is a method of proof used to prove infinite sequences of statements. An infinite sequence of statements is a collection of statements, each of which corresponds to one of the natural numbers. Let N be the set of natural numbers and write a_n for the statement corresponding to n, if $n \in N$. The problem of induction is to find a justification for inferring every one of the infinitely many statements

$$a_0, a_1, a_2, a_3, \ldots, a_n, \ldots,$$

given the premises

$$(1)\ a_0, \qquad (2)\ (\forall n \in N)(a_n \Rightarrow a_{n+1}).$$

The conclusion may be written

$$(\forall n \in N)(a_n).$$

Thus the assumptions are (1) the initial statement, and (2) each statement implies its immediate successor. The object is to prove that every one of the statements follows from these assumptions. Induction may be considered to differ from some of our previous examples of inferences because there are infinitely many conclusions, instead of the usual one.

One might be tempted to argue as follows. Given the premises a_0 and $a_0 \Rightarrow a_1$, infer a_1. Next, from a_1 and $a_1 \Rightarrow a_2$, infer a_2, etc. Thus we can construct a chain of inferences yielding at each step one of the statements in the sequence. It is quite clear that with a sufficiently long chain, we can reach any particular statement we may select, and it is just as clear that no finite chain will accomplish what we require: which is, of course, a proof for *all* of the infinitely many statements. The simple requirement that proofs must come to an end shows that this attempt to justify the inference is doomed to failure.

If we relax our requirement and demand only that some finite subset of the statements be deduced, then such a chain of inferences will suffice. If we were satisfied with deducing, for example, only five or ten or a million of the statements, we would be done. Our only obstacle is the demand that infinitely many statements be deduced. We shall prove (Theorem 1) that the inference can indeed be justified, and we shall find that the proof does not involve the chain of inferences which figured so prominently in our unsuccessful attempt.

Theorem 1 (*Principle of Mathematical Induction*). If

$$a_0, a_1, a_2, \ldots, a_n, \ldots$$

is a sequence of statements, the conclusion

$$(\forall n \in N)(a_n)$$

follows from the premises

$$a_0, \quad \text{and} \quad (\forall n \in N)(a_n \Rightarrow a_{n+1}).$$

This time, of course, we have to give a proof that can be written down in its entirety.

Proof. For our proof we appeal to the fact that N is well ordered. We argue by contradiction: If $(\exists n \in N)(\tilde{a}_n)$, then the set $\{n \in N : \tilde{a}_n\}$ of natural numbers is nonvoid. But each nonvoid subset of N has a least member; suppose m is the least member of $\{n \in N : \tilde{a}_n\}$. Then a_m is false and a_n is true if n is any natural number less than m. If $m = 0$, then a_0 is false, contradicting our first premise. If $m > 0$, then $m - 1$ is a natural number less than m. So a_{m-1} is true while a_m is false, and this contradicts the second premise, that each member of the sequence implies its immediate successor. This pair of contradictions completes the proof.

We illustrate the application of Theorem 1 by considering some examples.

Example 1 For each natural number n, $n < 2^n$.
Observe first that the inequality holds for $n = 0$: $0 < 2^0$, that is, $0 < 1$. It remains to prove, then, that $n + 1 < 2^{n+1}$ *if* $n < 2^n$. But this is easy:

$$n + 1 < 2^n + 1 \leq 2^n + 2^n = 2 \cdot 2^n = 2^{n+1},$$

where the first inequality follows from the "induction hypothesis," $n < 2^n$, and the second from the fact that 1 is the smallest positive integer.

Example 2 For $n \geq 2$,

$$1 + 2 + \cdots + (n - 1) < \frac{n^2}{2} < 1 + 2 + \cdots + n.$$

We choose our sequence of statements as follows:

$$a_0: \quad 1 < 2 < 3 \qquad (n = 2),$$
$$a_1: \quad 3 < 4.5 < 6 \qquad (n = 3),$$
$$a_2: \quad 6 < 8 < 10 \qquad (n = 4),$$
$$a_3: \quad 10 < 12.5 < 15 \qquad (n = 5),$$

etc.; and since a_0 is certainly true, we turn to the "inductive step" and prove that, for $n \geq 2$,

$$1 + 2 + \cdots + n < \frac{(n + 1)^2}{2} < 1 + 2 + \cdots + (n + 1)$$

if

$$1 + 2 + \cdots + (n - 1) < \frac{n^2}{2} < 1 + 2 + \cdots + n.$$

From

$$1 + 2 + \cdots + (n - 1) < \frac{n^2}{2},$$

we infer

$$1 + 2 + \cdots + n < \frac{n^2}{2} + n,$$

and from

$$\frac{n^2}{2} < 1 + 2 + \cdots + n,$$

we infer

$$\frac{n^2}{2} + (n + 1) < 1 + 2 + \cdots + (n + 1);$$

that is,

$$1 + 2 + \cdots + n < \frac{n^2 + 2n}{2}$$

and

$$\frac{n^2 + 2n + 2}{2} < 1 + 2 + \cdots + (n + 1).$$

But

$$\frac{n^2 + 2n}{2} < \frac{n^2 + 2n + 1}{2} < \frac{n^2 + 2n + 2}{2},$$

and we conclude that

$$1 + 2 + \cdots + n < \frac{(n + 1)^2}{2} < 1 + 2 + \cdots + (n + 1),$$

as required.

Example 3

$$\left(1 - \frac{1}{2}\right)\left(1 - \frac{1}{3}\right)\cdots\left(1 - \frac{1}{n}\right) = \frac{1}{n}, \quad \text{if} \quad n > 1.$$

For $n = 2$, we have $1 - \frac{1}{2} = \frac{1}{2}$. For any n greater than or equal to 2,

$$\left(1 - \frac{1}{2}\right)\left(1 - \frac{1}{3}\right)\cdots\left(1 - \frac{1}{n}\right) = \frac{1}{n}$$

implies

$$\left(1 - \frac{1}{2}\right)\left(1 - \frac{1}{3}\right)\cdots\left(1 - \frac{1}{n}\right)\left(1 - \frac{1}{n+1}\right) = \frac{1}{n}\left(1 - \frac{1}{n+1}\right).$$

But

$$\frac{1}{n}\left(1 - \frac{1}{n+1}\right) = \frac{1}{n}\frac{n+1-1}{n+1} = \frac{1}{n+1};$$

so

$$\left(1 - \frac{1}{2}\right)\left(1 - \frac{1}{3}\right)\cdots\left(1 - \frac{1}{n+1}\right) = \frac{1}{n+1}$$

follows; and we are done.

Example 4 If n and m are integers, n nonnegative, the numbers

$$\binom{n}{m} = \frac{n!}{m!(n-m)!} \quad \text{for} \quad 0 \leq m \leq n,$$
$$= 0 \quad \text{for} \quad m < 0 \quad \text{or} \quad n < m,$$

are called *binomial coefficients*. [For positive n, $n!$ is the product,

$$1 \cdot 2 \cdot 3 \cdots (n - 1)n,$$

of all positive integers up to, and including, n. Thus $1! = 1$, $2! = 2$, $3! = 6$, $4! = 24$, $5! = 120$, etc. $0!$ is defined to be 1. Observe, in particular, that $n! = n(n - 1)!$.] We prove, by induction, that every binomial coefficient is a natural number. For convenience we shall refer to n as the "order" of the binomial coefficient $\binom{n}{m}$. There is only one nonzero binomial coefficient of order zero: $\binom{0}{0} = 1$. [There are two nonzero binomial coefficients of order 1 and they are both 1: $\binom{1}{0} = 1$, $\binom{1}{1} = 1$.] We base the inductive step on the formula

$$\binom{n}{m} = \binom{n-1}{m} + \binom{n-1}{m-1},$$

which implies that each binomial coefficient of order n is the sum of a pair of binomial coefficients of order $n - 1$. Thus assuming that each one of order $n - 1$ is a natural number, it follows that all those of order n are as well. All that remains to be done is to prove the formula:

$$\binom{n-1}{m} + \binom{n-1}{m-1} = \frac{(n-1)!}{m!(n-1-m)!} + \frac{(n-1)!}{(m-1)!(n-1-(m-1))!}$$

$$= \frac{(n-1)!}{m!(n-m-1)!} + \frac{(n-1)!}{(m-1)!(n-m)!}$$

$$= \frac{(n-1)!(n-m)}{m!(n-m)!} + \frac{m(n-1)!}{m!(n-m)!}$$

$$= \frac{(n-1)!}{m!(n-m)!}(n-m+m)$$

$$= \frac{n!}{m!(n-m)!}$$

$$= \binom{n}{m}.$$

Other Forms of Mathematical Induction

In the proof of Theorem 1 we invoked the well ordering of N. An examination of the argument will reveal that with only a few quite minor changes, we can extend the proof to cover some very important variations of the principle of induction.

We obtained our contradictions when, after having used the well ordering of N to get a false statement preceded only by true ones, we observed that the false one could be deduced from one of the true ones preceding it. Actually we deduced it from its immediate predecessor, but we could, of course, obtain the same contradiction if we deduced it from any one of its predecessors. Moreover, if it is possible to deduce a_m from some one of its predecessors, it is also possible to deduce it from the conjunction of *all* of them: since, from T-2, page 25.

$$a_0 \wedge a_1 \wedge a_2 \wedge \cdots \wedge a_{m-1} \Rightarrow a_k,$$

for any natural number k less than m.

We are thus led to formulate a second version of the principle of mathematical induction.

Theorem 2 If $a_0, a_1, a_2, \ldots, a_n, \ldots$ is a sequence of statements, the conclusion

$$(\forall n \in N)(a_n)$$

follows from the premises

$$a_0 \quad \text{and} \quad (\forall n \in N)[A_n \Rightarrow a_n],$$

where A_n is the conjunction $a_0 \wedge a_1 \wedge \cdots \wedge a_{n-1}$ of all members of the sequence preceding a_n.

We leave, as an exercise, the task of writing out a proof for Theorem 2 based on the well ordering of N. Observe, however, that Theorem 1 is an immediate corollary of Theorem 2, for from the assumption

$$(\forall n \in N)[a_n \Rightarrow a_{n+1}],$$

it follows immediately that

$$(\forall n \in N)[A_{n+1} \Rightarrow a_{n+1}]$$

and so, using Theorem 2, we may infer each of the statements $a_0, a_1, \ldots, a_n, \ldots$. We leave, as another exercise, the proof that Theorem 2 is also a corollary of Theorem 1 and turn, instead, to some applications of Theorem 2.

Example 5   The Fibonacci numbers F_n are defined as follows:

$$F_0 = 1, \qquad F_1 = 1, \qquad F_n = F_{n-1} + F_{n-2} \qquad \text{for} \quad n > 1.$$

Thus

$$F_2 = 1 + 1 = 2, \qquad F_3 = 1 + 2 = 3,$$
$$F_4 = 2 + 3 = 5, \qquad F_5 = 3 + 5 = 8,$$
$$F_6 = 5 + 8 = 13, \qquad F_7 = 8 + 13 = 21,$$
$$F_8 = 13 + 21 = 34, \qquad F_9 = 21 + 34 = 55,$$

etc. Prove that, for $n > 1$,

$$\alpha^{n-1} < F_n < \alpha^n \qquad \text{if} \qquad \alpha = \tfrac{1}{2}(1 + \sqrt{5}).$$

Note first that $1 < \alpha < 2$ and $\alpha^2 = \alpha + 1$. The first statement ($n = 2$) is

$$\alpha < 2 < \alpha^2 = \alpha + 1.$$

Adding 1 across the inequality, we get

$$\alpha + 1 < 3 < \alpha^2 + 1.$$

But $\alpha + 1 = \alpha^2$ and $\alpha^2 + 1 < \alpha^2 + \alpha = \alpha^3$; hence

$$\alpha^2 < 3 < \alpha^3,$$

which is the second statement ($n = 3$). For $n > 3$ we use the formula

$$F_n = F_{n-1} + F_{n-2}.$$

As our inductive hypothesis we assume

$$\alpha^{k-1} < F_k < \alpha^k$$

for each k between 2 and n. Then, in particular,

$$\alpha^{n-2} < F_{n-1} < \alpha^{n-1}$$

and
$$\alpha^{n-3} < F_{n-2} < \alpha^{n-2},$$
so
$$\alpha^{n-2} + \alpha^{n-3} < F_{n-1} + F_{n-2} < \alpha^{n-1} + \alpha^{n-2}$$
which, since $\alpha^2 = \alpha + 1$, gives
$$\alpha^{n-1} < F_n < \alpha^n.$$

Example 6 Given that a natural number n greater than 1 is a prime if it cannot be factored into a product of two natural numbers each of which is less than n, prove that every natural number greater than 1 is either a prime or a product of primes.

Proof. First we observe that 2 is a prime. Then, if n is greater than 1 and not a prime, it can be factored into a product of two natural numbers each of which is greater than 1 [why?] and less than n. By the induction hypothesis each of these factors of n is either a prime or a product of primes, and it follows that n, being their product, is itself a product of primes.

Example 7 A famous theorem in the theory of numbers is the theorem that every natural number can be expressed as a sum of four squares.

As examples of such expressions we have

$$0 = 0^2 + 0^2 + 0^2 + 0^2, \quad 1 = 1^2 + 0^2 + 0^2 + 0^2,$$
$$2 = 1^2 + 1^2 + 0^2 + 0^2, \quad 3 = 1^2 + 1^2 + 1^2 + 0^2,$$
$$4 = 2^2 + 0^2 + 0^2 + 0^2, \quad 5 = 2^2 + 1^2 + 0^2 + 0^2,$$
$$6 = 2^2 + 1^2 + 1^2 + 0^2, \quad 7 = 2^2 + 1^2 + 1^2 + 1^2,$$
$$8 = 2^2 + 2^2 + 0^2 + 0^2, \quad 9 = 3^2 + 0^2 + 0^2 + 0^2,$$

This theorem is proved by induction as follows. The identity

$$(a^2 + b^2 + c^2 + d^2)(w^2 + x^2 + y^2 + z^2)$$
$$= (aw + bx + cy + dz)^2 + (ax - bw - cz + dy)^2$$
$$+ (ay + bz - cw - dx)^2 + (az - by + cx - dw)^2,$$

which is due to Euler, shows that if two numbers can be expressed as a sum of four squares, then the same thing is true of their product. Since each natural number greater than 1 is either a prime or a product of primes, the proof of the theorem can be completed by showing that every prime may be expressed as a sum of four squares, a difficult result first proved by Lagrange.

In our original principle of induction, the inductive step consists of inferring a_n from its immediate predecessor a_{n-1}: in the example involving the Fibonacci numbers we infer a_n from the conjunction $a_{n-2} \land a_{n-1}$ of the two immediate predecessors of a_n, but in the last two examples a_n is inferred from one or more predecessors of a_n—but just which ones (or how many of them) depends on n. For example,

$$a_2 \Rightarrow a_4,$$
$$a_2 \wedge a_3 \Rightarrow a_6,$$
$$a_2 \Rightarrow a_8,$$
$$a_3 \Rightarrow a_9,$$
$$a_2 \wedge a_5 \Rightarrow a_{10},$$
$$a_2 \wedge a_3 \Rightarrow a_{12},$$
$$a_2 \wedge a_7 \Rightarrow a_{14},$$
$$a_3 \wedge a_5 \Rightarrow a_{15}.$$
$$\text{etc.}$$

There are other important versions of mathematical induction. Those we have considered here are classified as *finite induction*, or *complete induction*, referring to the fact that in a sequence each member has only finitely many predecessors. A sequence of statements is given by a function whose domain is the set of natural numbers and whose values are statements. Consider a statement-valued function f defined on an arbitrary well-ordered set A. Write $\leq$ for the order relation under which A is assumed to be well ordered. If, for each a in A, $f(a)$ is a consequence of

$$(\forall x \in A)[(x < a) \Rightarrow f(x)],$$

the *principle of transfinite induction* justifies the conclusion $(\forall x \in A)f(x)$. The proof does not differ essentially from that proof of Theorem 2 which uses the fact that N is well ordered.

EXERCISES

Give induction proofs for the assertions in Exercises 1 through 15.

1. $1^2 + 2^2 + \cdots + (n-1)^2 < \dfrac{n^3}{3} < 1^2 + 2^2 + \cdots + n^2$, if $n \geq 2$

2. $1^3 + 2^3 + \cdots + (n-1)^3 < \dfrac{n^4}{4} < 1^3 + 2^3 + \cdots + n^3$, if $n \geq 2$

3. $1^4 + 2^4 + \cdots + (n-1)^4 < \dfrac{n^5}{5} < 1^4 + 2^4 + \cdots + n^4$, if $n \geq 2$

4. $1 \cdot 2 + 2 \cdot 3 + \cdots + n(n+1) = \dfrac{n(n+1)(n+2)}{3}$, if $n \geq 1$

5. $1 \cdot 2 \cdot 3 + 2 \cdot 3 \cdot 4 + \cdots + n(n+1)(n+2)$

$$= \dfrac{n(n+1)(n+2)(n+3)}{4}, \quad \text{if} \quad n \geq 1$$

6. $1 \cdot 2 \cdot 3 \cdot 4 + 2 \cdot 3 \cdot 4 \cdot 5 + \cdots + n(n+1)(n+2)(n+3)$

$$= \frac{n(n+1)(n+2)(n+3)(n+4)}{5}, \quad \text{if} \quad n \geq 1$$

7. $\dfrac{1}{1 \cdot 2} + \dfrac{1}{2 \cdot 3} + \cdots + \dfrac{1}{n(n+1)} = \dfrac{n}{n+1}, \quad \text{if} \quad n \geq 1$

8. $1 \cdot 1! + 2 \cdot 2! + \cdots + n \cdot n! = (n+1)! - 1, \quad \text{if} \quad n \geq 1$

9. $\dfrac{1}{1^2} + \dfrac{1}{2^2} + \cdots + \dfrac{1}{n^2} < 2 - \dfrac{1}{n}, \quad \text{if} \quad n \geq 2$

10. $2^n < n!, \quad \text{if} \quad n \geq 4$

11. $n^2 < 2^n, \quad \text{if} \quad n \geq 5$

12. $1 + a + a^2 + \cdots + a^{n-1} = \dfrac{a^n - 1}{a - 1}, \quad \text{if} \quad n \geq 1$

13. $\alpha^n = \alpha^{n-1} + \alpha^{n-2} \quad \text{for} \quad \alpha = \frac{1}{2}(1 \pm \sqrt{5}), \quad \text{if} \quad n \geq 2$

14. $(1 + a)^n \geq 1 + na \quad \text{for} \quad a \geq 0, \quad \text{if} \quad n \geq 0$

15. $(1 + a)^n \geq 1 + na + \frac{1}{2}n(n-1)a^2 \quad \text{for} \quad a \geq 0, \quad \text{if} \quad n \geq 0$

16. Prove Theorem 2, (a) by appealing directly to the fact that N is well ordered, and (b) by deducing it as a corollary of Theorem 1.

APPENDIX

CONSISTENCY AND
THE CONSTRUCTION OF MODELS

Given a set of postulates for a mathematical system, there are two possibilities: either there is a pair of statements, one the negation of the other, both of which can be deduced from the set of postulates, or there is no such pair. In the latter case, the set of postulates is said to be *consistent*, and in the former case, *inconsistent*. Inconsistent sets of postulates are useless: every statement may be deduced from them,

$$(p \wedge \tilde{p}) \Rightarrow q \equiv \tilde{p} \vee p \vee q \equiv I \vee q \equiv I,$$

and therefore the collection of "systems" they describe is void. (Unless there is something you cannot say about it, you aren't talking about anything at all.) Thus it is important to be able to decide whether or not a given set of postulates is consistent. One common method for proving consistency is relative, and takes the form of proving that the postulates for one system are consistent, provided those for some other system are consistent. The technique used is to construct in the second system a model of the first system.

One of the questions, for example, appropriate for consideration in a study of the logical foundations of mathematics is whether or not any of the postulate systems (like those in Chapter 4) for the elementary number systems is actually consistent. It is possible, and indeed not very difficult, to prove that the postulates for the complex number system are consistent provided those for the real number system are consistent, and that these in turn are consistent provided those for the rational number system are consistent, that the postulates for the rationals are consistent if those for the integers are, and that the postulates for the integers are consistent if the postulates for the natural number system are. These proofs are accomplished by constructing a model of each system using members of the next system. Indeed, complex numbers can be "constructed" as ordered pairs of real numbers, real numbers as Dedekind sections or as classes of Cantor sequences of rational numbers, rational numbers as classes of equivalent fractions (which are ordered pairs of integers), and integers as classes of differences (again, ordered pairs) of natural numbers. Important as it may be to determine whether the postulates for a number system are consistent, or that they are consistent provided those for some other system are consistent, consistency proofs do not afford any real insight into the nature or the properties of the numbers of the system: they show only that the system has at least one model, or that it has one if some other system does. A more profound project, in the case of the number systems, is the construction of postulate sets for each system which are not only consistent but which are categorical as well. The constructions referred to above show that, except (possibly) for the natural number system, each number system has at least one model of some kind; if its postulates are categorical, the system has at most one model (in the sense that all models are isomorphic). But, being isomorphic, all models are essentially the "same," no matter how they may be constructed, which suggests that the actual details of such constructions can have very little to reveal about the "true nature" (whatever that may mean) of the various kinds of numbers. The same observations apply, of course, to von Neumann's set-theoretical counterfeit of the natural number system (Chapter 2), and indicate that it is just as far-fetched to assert that (natural) numbers *are* sets as it is to assert that integers *are* classes of pairs of natural numbers, etc. Unfortunately, however, there are some among us (including teachers of the young) who seem to believe that such assertions not only make sense, but that they actually convey valuable information about the various kinds of numbers and what they really are.

AXIOMATIC SET THEORY

One may well be tempted to regard the von Neumann construction (or any other set-theoretical construction for the natural numbers) as a giant step backward, because it shifts the question of consistency from the natural number system to set theory: from a simple and more familiar system to a complicated and more mysterious one. Set theory is not without problems of its own—as Russell showed, for example, with his paradox. Hence the urge, if not the necessity, to put set theory itself in axiomatic form and to determine what might be required to make the theory elaborate enough to serve as a foundation for the construction of models for other parts of mathematics.*

---

* The claim that it is possible to reduce all of mathematics to set theory is known among philosophers of mathematics as the *logistic* or *Frege-Russell thesis*; there is some disagreement on whether the claim has actually been substantiated, or even if it can ever be. It cannot be disputed, however, that attacks on the problem have produced many important results.

By restricting the specification principle to the determination of subsets of a given set we seem to avoid the Russell paradox in particular, but it is difficult to be very confident that we have ruled out the possibility that some contradiction may still appear in the system.

Axiomatic set theorists set down lists of axioms about sets which are designed to authorize the construction of sets sufficiently complicated to carry out the reduction of mathematics to set theory. Such lists have been proposed by various writers; they differ from one another in some respects, but most have several quite basic axioms in common. Here we outline a fragment of the theory, discussing only six axioms: those used for the development of elementary mathematics, and in particular for the construction of cartesian products and the number systems.

Among some of the more commonly proposed axioms are

the principle of extensionality

and

the specification principle,

which we have discussed previously: one provides a criterion for equality of sets, the other permits conditions to characterize subsets of given sets. Several of the other axioms are concerned with the question of just what is a "given" set. One modest observation is this: if any set "exists," the void set does. [*Proof.* Apply the specification principle to the given set using the condition expressed by the open sentence $x \neq x$. The extension of this condition in the given set is $\emptyset$.] One of the axioms we shall state later (*the axiom of infinity*) will indeed assert that some set does "exist," but for the time being it turns out there is a good deal we can accomplish merely by assuming that $\emptyset$ is a set.

Axiom of pairing Given any two sets, there is a set whose members are the given sets.

Using this axiom, we may conclude that $\{\emptyset\}$ is a set (taking $\emptyset$ for both of the given sets), and hence that $\{\{\emptyset\}\}$, $\{\emptyset; \{\emptyset\}\}$, and a great variety of similar combinations are sets.

Axiom of unions Given any collection of sets, there is a set whose members are all elements which belong to at least one of the given sets.

Thus, for example, if U and V are given sets, $U \cup V$ is a set. It turns out that we do not require a similar axiom for intersections. We can get by with those we have already.

Theorem If C is a nonvoid collection of sets, there is a set D which is a subset of every member of C and which contains every element which is a member of every member of C.

Proof. C is not void. Let $A \in C$. With A as universe, apply the specification principle, using the condition $(\forall X \in C)(x \in X)$ and call its extension D. Then $x \in D$ if and only if $(\forall X \in C)(x \in X)$.

We state one more axiom at this point and then consider the question of the "existence" of ordered couples and cartesian products.

Axiom of powers Given any set, there is a set whose members are all the subsets of the given set.

These axioms may all appear to be innocent enough—and perhaps they really are, no one can say for sure. In any event, it was no mean intellectual feat to extract as much from them as clever men have managed to get. Here we consider couples and products. Finally we shall assert that one can produce numbers with the help of one further axiom.

Couples and Products

We restrict our attention here to ordered couples of sets. If a and b are sets, the axiom of pairing tells us that $\{a\}$ and $\{a, b\}$ are also sets, and the same axiom tells us that $\{\{a\}, \{a, b\}\}$ is a set.

Definition $(a, b) = \{\{a\}, \{a, b\}\}$.

This is a nice, short, definition; but we face the problem of deciding why $\{\{a\}, \{a, b\}\}$ deserves to be called an ordered couple. If we look back at our earlier discussion of ordered couples, we find there is really only one thing we required of an ordered couple, whatever it may be. We required that we be able to tell which component was "first" and which was "second." We expressed this requirement in our criterion for equality:

$$(a, b) = (c, d) \qquad \text{if and only if} \qquad a = c \quad \text{and} \quad b = d.$$

Does our definition satisfy this criterion? The "if" part follows directly from the principle of extensionality:

if $\qquad\qquad\qquad\quad a = c \qquad \text{and} \qquad b = d,$

then $\qquad\qquad\qquad \{a\} = \{c\} \qquad \text{and} \qquad \{a, b\} = \{c, d\},$

so $\qquad\qquad\qquad\qquad \{\{a\}, \{a, b\}\} = \{\{c\}, \{c, d\}\};$

that is, $\qquad\qquad\qquad\qquad\qquad (a, b) = (c, d).$

For the converse, suppose $(a, b) = (c, d)$, that is,

$$\{\{a\}, \{a, b\}\} = \{\{c\}, \{c, d\}\}.$$

To show that $a = c$ and $b = d$, we consider two cases.

First, suppose $b = a$. Then (a, b) is the singleton $\{\{a\}\}$. If $(a, b) = (c, d)$, then (c, d) is a singleton too; but $\{c\} = \{c, d\}$ means $c = d$, so

$(c, d) = \{\{c\}\}$.   Finally $\{\{a\}\} = \{\{c\}\}$ implies $\{a\} = \{c\}$ and hence $a = c$.

For the second case, we assume $b \neq a$. Then (a, b) is not a singleton, and hence (c, d) is not either. But (a, b) and (c, d) each contain just one singleton: $\{a\}$ and $\{c\}$, respectively. It follows that $\{a\} = \{c\}$ and $a = c$. Also (a, b) and (c, d) each contain just one nonsingleton, consequently $\{a, b\} = \{c, d\}$. Hence $b \in \{c, d\}$, but $b \neq c$, since $a = c$ and $b \neq a$; so $b = d$.   Q.E.D.

Finally we construct products as follows. Suppose A and B are given nonvoid sets. We want a set containing each couple (a, b) where $a \in A$ and $b \in B$. First $a \in A$, $b \in B$ imply $\{a\} \subseteq A$, $\{b\} \subseteq B$, and hence $\{a\}$, $\{b\}$, and $\{a, b\}$ are all subsets of $A \cup B$. Thus $\{a\}$ and $\{a, b\}$ are members of the set of subsets of $A \cup B$, and it follows that $\{\{a\}, \{a, b\}\}$ is a subset of the set of subsets of $A \cup B$, that is, $\{\{a\}, \{a, b\}\}$ is an element of the set of subsets of the set of subsets of $A \cup B$. We have found a set containing each (a, b) as a member, where a is any member of A and b is any member of B. The set we have found does, of course, contain many other elements as well. We cut them out with the specification principle using the condition $(\exists a \in A)(\exists b \in B)[x = (a, b)]$, whose extension we define to be $A \times B$.

Numbers

Von Neumann's construction of the natural numbers proceeds as follows: Consider the sets

$$\varnothing, \ \{\varnothing\}, \ \{\varnothing, \{\varnothing\}\}, \ \{\varnothing, \{\varnothing\}, \{\varnothing, \{\varnothing\}\}\}, \ \ldots$$

Given the void set to start with, the axioms of pairing and of unions permit us to construct these sets one after another: for if A is any set in this list, the next set is $A \cup \{A\}$. Von Neumann named these sets as follows: let 0 be $\varnothing$, 1 be $\{\varnothing\}$, 2 be $\{\varnothing, \{\varnothing\}\}$, 3 be $\{\varnothing, \{\varnothing\}, \{\varnothing, \{\varnothing\}\}\}$, etc. Then $1 = \{0\}$, $2 = \{0, 1\}$, $3 = \{0, 1, 2\}$, etc., and the list above is

$$0, \ 1, \ 2, \ 3, \ \ldots$$

The question now is whether this construction can be carried "far enough" to get all the "natural numbers"; according to the axiom of infinity, the answer is *yes*.

Axiom of infinity There is a set with the following properties:

(1) $\varnothing$ is a member,

(2) if A is any member, $A \cup \{A\}$ is also a member.

So, the things exist. One can define addition and multiplication for von Neumann's "numbers" and prove that, with these operations, they have every property one is entitled to expect numbers to have. Given these "nonnegative integers," one can go on to build "negative integers," "rational numbers," "real numbers," and "complex numbers": numbers of each of these types being certain collections of numbers of the preceding type (or collections of collections of them, etc.). Hence the claim that mathematics can be founded on the theory of sets, and the corollary that the only sets one need consider are sets whose members, if any, are themselves sets.

A SHORT LIST OF BOOKS

Paul R. Halmos, *Naive Set Theory*. Van Nostrand, 1960.

D. Hilbert and W. Ackermann, *Principles of Mathematical Logic*. Chelsea, 1950.

Franz E. Hohn, *Applied Boolean Algebra*. Macmillan, 1966 (second edition).

D. E. Rutherford, *Introduction to Lattice Theory*. Oliver & Boyd/Hafner, 1965.

Robert R. Stoll, *Set Theory and Logic*. Freeman, 1963.

Raymond L. Wilder, *Introduction to the Foundations of Mathematics*. Wiley, 1965 (second edition).

INDEX

173

SYLLOGISMS, p. 97

A: $(\forall x)[\alpha(x) \Rightarrow \beta(x)]$
I: $(\exists x)[\alpha(x) \wedge \beta(x)]$

E: $(\forall x)[\alpha(x) \Rightarrow \tilde{\beta}(x)]$
O: $(\exists x)[\alpha(x) \wedge \tilde{\beta}(x)]$

I	II	III	IV
M P	P M	M P	P M
S M	S M	M S	M S
$\therefore$ S P	$\therefore$ S P	$\therefore$ S P	$\therefore$ S P

BARBARA	CESARE	DATISI	CALEMES
CELARENT	CAMESTRES	FERISO	FRESISON
DARII	FESTINO	DISAMIS	DIMATIS
FERIO	BAROCO	BOCARDO	*BAMALIP (P)
		*DARAPTI (M)	*FESAPO (M)
		*FELAPTON (M)	

CHANGE OF SCOPE, pp. 105, 106

A1. $(\forall x)[\pi(x) \wedge \rho(x)] \Leftrightarrow (\forall x)\pi(x) \wedge (\forall x)\rho(x)$
A2. $(\exists x)[\pi(x) \vee \rho(x)] \Leftrightarrow (\exists x)\pi(x) \vee (\exists x)\rho(x)$
A3. $(\exists x)[\pi(x) \Rightarrow \rho(x)] \Leftrightarrow [(\forall x)\pi(x) \Rightarrow (\exists x)\rho(x)]$

B1. $(\forall x)\pi(x) \vee (\forall x)\rho(x) \Rightarrow (\forall x)[\pi(x) \vee \rho(x)]$
B2. $(\exists x)[\pi(x) \wedge \rho(x)] \Rightarrow (\exists x)\pi(x) \wedge (\exists x)\rho(x)$
B3. $[(\exists x)\pi(x) \Rightarrow (\forall x)\rho(x)] \Rightarrow (\forall x)[\pi(x) \Rightarrow \rho(x)]$

C1. $(\forall x)[\pi(x) \Rightarrow \rho(x)] \Rightarrow [(\forall x)\pi(x) \Rightarrow (\forall x)\rho(x)]$
C2. $[(\exists x)\pi(x) \Rightarrow (\exists x)\rho(x)] \Rightarrow (\exists x)[\pi(x) \Rightarrow \rho(x)]$ $\qquad (U \neq \varnothing)$

D1. $(\forall x)[\pi(x) \vee \rho(x)] \Rightarrow [(\forall x)\pi(x) \vee (\exists x)\rho(x)]$
D2. $[(\exists x)\pi(x) \wedge (\forall x)\rho(x)] \Rightarrow (\exists x)[\pi(x) \wedge \rho(x)]$
D3. $(\forall x)[\pi(x) \Rightarrow \rho(x)] \Rightarrow [(\exists x)\pi(x) \Rightarrow (\exists x)\rho(x)]$

E1. $(\forall x)[\pi(x) \Leftrightarrow \rho(x)] \Rightarrow [(\forall x)\pi(x) \Leftrightarrow (\forall x)\rho(x)]$
E2. $(\forall x)[\pi(x) \Leftrightarrow \rho(x)] \Rightarrow [(\exists x)\pi(x) \Leftrightarrow (\exists x)\rho(x)]$